JUICING
TO HEAL

Transform your Health
and Heal Naturally

K. GRIFFITHS RN MSN, ED FNP-C

Health

- The author of this book does not dispense medical advice or prescribe the use of any technique as a form of treatment for physical, emotional, or medical problems without the advice of a physician, either directly or indirectly. The intent of the author is only to offer information of a general nature to help you in your quest for emotional, physical, and spiritual well-being. In the event you use any of the information in this book for yourself, the author and the publisher assume no responsibility for your actions.
- This book is not intended as a substitute for the medical advice of physicians. The reader should regularly consult a physician in matters relating to his/her health and particularly with respect to any symptoms that may require diagnosis or medical attention.
- This book is solely for information and educational purposes and does not constitute medical advice. Please consult a medical or health professional before you begin any exercise, nutrition, or supplementation program or if you have questions about your health.

CONTENTS

INTRODUCTION

Did you know a single glass of juice can contain the vitamins and minerals in several servings of fruits and vegetables? It's true!

Juicing is more than just a trendy health craze. It is a powerful way to provide your body with nutrients and improve your overall well-being.

This cookbook explores the benefits of juicing and how it can be a delicious tool to improve your health. Of course, this book would not be complete without tasty recipes. So, I am giving you more than 70 tasty juice recipes to heal your body from the inside out.

With so much misinformation going around about juicing, it's time to set the record straight. There are thousands of juicing books out there promising to heal your ailments. However, they are filled with complex recipes that don't taste good. You need hard-to-find ingredients and special equipment to make them.

They contain ingredients that may worsen your condition. The recipes probably didn't even contain nutritional information. They probably focused on weight loss instead of common illnesses like heart disease, diabetes, or stroke.

This cookbook is the opposite of that. It is filled with simple, easy-to-make recipes. These recipes are made using everyday ingredients. You won't find the same recipes repeated over and over again. I get tired of drinking the same juice over and over again, so I created a variety of flavorful recipes to target different diseases.

All of the ingredients have been thoroughly researched to ensure that there is scientific proof to back them up. The recipes contain accurate nutritional information, so you know exactly what you are putting into your body. While this cookbook can help you lose weight, it is not the book's main focus. You will find recipes that heal arthritis, high cholesterol, gout, and more.

I know what you are thinking. Why should I listen to you when the juicing books I have read have not been helpful? I am a registered nurse with more than 28 years of experience in the field. I believe that our bodies are special. We can heal ourselves as long as we have the right tools to do so.

I am passionate about using juicing to heal your body from the inside out. I am meticulous. I have spent hours researching ingredients to help heal certain diseases. I have tried every juicer on the market.

I have spent countless hours in the kitchen testing different combinations to create flavorful and nutrient-dense juices. I have made it my mission to educate others on the healing power of juicing. I recognize the nutritional powerhouses that fruits and veggies are, and I incorporate juicing into my life every chance I get.

Promoting health and wellness is my life. I encourage my patients to explore the healing power of juicing. That is how I came to create this book.

I hope this book will transform your life. So, grab your juicer and get ready to dive into a new world of healthy, flavorful, and healing juicing!

WHAT IS JUICING

Juicing is a process that removes the liquid (juice) from fruits and vegetables, leaving pulp behind. This can be done using a juicer or blender. These tools will break down the produce into a smooth liquid, leaving behind the pulp.

Juicing allows you to consume a concentrated source of nutrients from fruits and vegetables in an easily digestible form. Juicing is a popular way to increase the amount of nutrients you consume. It can also help you remove toxins from your body.

Juicing is an easy way to add different fruits and veggies to your diet. It is also a great way to get your nutrients if you cannot eat whole fruits and vegetables in large quantities.

WHAT CAN I JUICE

You can juice several fruits, vegetables, and even herbs to create delicious and nutritious beverages. Here are some examples of foods you can juice:

FRUITS

- Apples
- Oranges
- Berries (strawberries, blueberries, blackberries, raspberries)
- Pineapple
- Grapes
- Kiwi
- Watermelon
- Mango
- Pears
- Citrus fruits (lemons, oranges, limes, grapefruits)

VEGETABLES

- Leafy greens (spinach, kale, Swiss chard, collard greens)
- Carrots
- Celery
- Cabbage

- Broccoli
- Cauliflower
- Brussels sprouts
- Cucumbers
- Beets

- Bell peppers
- Tomatoes
- Fennel
- Parsley
- Wheatgrass

ROOTS & TUBERS

- Ginger
- Turmeric

- Sweet potatoes
- Carrots

- Beets
- Radishes

HERBS

- Mint
- Basil

- Cilantro
- Parsley

- Dill
- Rosemary

These are just a few examples of the many foods you can juice. Experimenting with different fruits, vegetables, and herbs will allow you to create unique flavors and tailor your juices to your personal preferences. Remember, be mindful of any allergies or sensitivities when selecting ingredients.

FOODS TO AVOID JUICING

While you can juice many fruits, vegetables, and herbs, there are a few foods you should stay away from. These foods are not recommended for juicing due to their texture, flavor, or potential health risks. Here are the foods you should never juice:

1. **Avocado:** Avocados have a creamy texture and high-fat content. So, you should never juice them. Instead, eat avocados whole or use them to make smoothies or dips.
2. **Bananas:** Bananas are another fruit that is not juiced. Like avocados, they have a thick and creamy texture. Technically, you can make banana juice. However, it will be very thick. Additionally, the banana may clog up the juicer blades while you are making juice.
3. **Coconut:** Coconut water is a popular beverage. However, the flesh of a coconut is not juiced due to its high fiber content and tough texture. Use Coconut flesh to make smoothies or coconut milk.

4. **Papaya Seeds:** You can juice papaya flesh, but you cannot juice papaya seeds. The seeds have a bitter taste. Papaya seeds can also contain compounds that can be toxic if eaten in large amounts. So leave them out of your juice.
5. **Certain Seeds and Pits:** Seeds and pits from fruits such as apples, cherries, mangoes, apricots, and peaches contain compounds that can be harmful if ingested in large amounts. It's best to remove seeds and pits before juicing these fruits.
6. **Rhubarb Leaves:** Rhubarb leaves contain oxalic acid. Oxalic acid can be toxic if you eat it in large quantities. Therefore, you should only juice the stalks and not the leaves.

By avoiding these foods, you can enjoy safe and delicious homemade juices that are both nutritious and refreshing.

We have discussed what juicing is. We have discussed which foods should and should not be juiced. Now, it is time to talk about the health benefits of juicing. So, turn the page and discover how juicing can benefit your health.

THE HEALTH BENEFITS OF JUICING

Juicing has been celebrated for many years. The ability to provide a concentrated dose of vitamins, minerals, and antioxidants in a delicious yet easily digestible form is simply a miracle.

This chapter will dive into the science behind juicing and its potential to support overall health and well-being, from boosting immune function to supporting digestion and promoting hydration. Juicing offers a wealth of benefits for the body and mind. You will discover how incorporating fresh juices into your daily routine can help you have a healthier, more vibrant life.

Juicing offers a range of potential benefits for health and well-being. Some of these benefits include:

INCREASED NUTRIENT INTAKE

Juicing produce provides the body with a strong cocktail containing vitamins, minerals, and antioxidants. For example, berries contain bioactive compounds like antioxidants. These compounds can prevent inflammation and lower the risk of various cancers (Fabjanowicz et al., 2024).

Vitamins are needed for growth and development (Stevens, 2021). Minerals play an important role in nearly all bodily processes, including metabolism (Abdullah Al Ali, 2023). Juicing can be an easy way to provide your body with these essential nutrients. It can also be an easy way to meet the daily nutritional requirements.

IMPROVED DIGESTION

Juicing takes the fiber out of fruits and vegetables. This makes it easier for the body to digest and absorb nutrients, which may benefit individuals with digestive issues. For example, pineapples contain bromelain. It is a group of enzymes that digest specific proteins, aiding the digestion and absorption of proteins (Indresh et al., 2022).

Additionally, fruits and vegetables help increase good gut bacteria (Bacteroides plebeius) (Henning et al., 2017). Good bacteria help your body absorb nutrients more easily. So juicing adds a variety of fruits and vegetables to your body, which gives the body the nutrients it needs to perform and help keep your gut healthy.

HYDRATION

Juicing helps increase your fluid intake. The more fluid you drink, the more hydrated you will be. Hydration is crucial for overall health. Moreover, hydration also plays a role in bodily functions.

Water transports important nutrients and oxygen to your cells. It helps maintain your body volume, prevents dehydration, helps maintain your core body temperature, and acts as a lubricant (Rodrigues et al., 2015). Fruits and vegetables are made up and contain a significant amount of water. Therefore, juicing can help keep you hydrated.

WEIGHT MANAGEMENT

Juicing can help you lose weight. Vegetable and fruit juices provide nutrients such as polyphenols and nitrates which can act like a prebiotic.

One 2017 study put 20 participants on a 3-day juice diet. The participants had an increase in good bacteria, which ultimately led to weight loss that lasted after the study concluded (Henning et al., 2017). Juicing helps you reach your weight loss goals.

However, juicing should be incorporated into a balanced diet. Do not skip meals. Drinking juice alone is not a healthy or sustainable way to lose weight.

INCREASED ENERGY

Fruits and vegetables are nutritional powerhouses. They contain vitamins, minerals, and antioxidants. For example, oranges contain vitamin B1 (Thiamine), which helps produce energy from carbohydrates and fats (Temitope, 2019). Riboflavin, which is abundant in leafy green vegetables, enables the conversion of carbohydrates, fats, and proteins into ATP (energy) (Tardy et al., 2020). Riboflavin provides the body with the energy it needs to carry out vital physiological processes. These same nutrients are found in fresh juice. They give the body a natural energy boost, which prevents fatigue.

IMPROVED SKIN HEALTH

Fruits and vegetables are a goldmine of antioxidants. The high levels of antioxidants can help protect your skin from damage from free radicals.

Free radicals are reactive molecules with one or more unpaired electrons in their outer shell. These unpaired electrons make free radicals unstable. As a result, free radicals can damage cells, DNA, and proteins in the body, leading to oxidative stress and various health problems.

One study found citrus juices can help decrease oxidative stress, which can help promote skin health (Kim et al., 2016). Additionally, pomegranates are also good for your skin. They have even been used to treat skin disorders. For example, pomegranates have antioxidants and anti-inflammatory phytochemicals, which can help treat human epidermal keratinocytes (Mahaveer & Prerak, 2019). Juicing can provide a wide array of nutrients that support skin health from the inside out. You can help protect your skin from harsh damage and maintain a healthy, youthful appearance.

SUPPORT FOR IMMUNE FUNCTION

Juicing provides a concentrated source of immune-boosting nutrients like vitamin C and antioxidants. These nutrients may support a healthy immune system. A healthy immune system can decrease your risk of getting an illness.

For example, citrus juices are rich in vitamin C and folate. These nutrients help support the immune system by protecting against inflammation and promoting the function of various immune cells (Miles & Calder, 2021). Therefore, juicing can help strengthen the body's natural defense mechanisms and help improve the body's ability to fight off infections and illnesses.

Additionally, juicing can aid in hydration. Hydration is essential for optimal immune functioning and may support detoxification processes that help rid the body of harmful toxins and pathogens.

Juicing has many health benefits. However, it's important to note that it is not a replacement for consuming whole fruits and vegetables. Whole fruits and vegetables provide fiber and other important nutrients. So make sure you strike a balance between juicing and eating whole produce.

Additionally, everybody's juicing experience is different. It's always a good idea to consult with a healthcare professional before making you start juicing.

Juicing has a lot of benefits. It has the power to transform your life. Now that we have discussed the benefits of juicing, it's time to discuss an important tool you will need to make juice.

The next chapter is a guide to buying the perfect juicer. You will learn about the types of juicers and the important factors to consider when buying a juicer. So turn the page, and let's go.

A GUIDE TO BUYING THE RIGHT JUICER

You cannot juice fruits and vegetables without a juicer. After all, a juicer is the tool that makes juicing so easy. But all juicers are not equal. There are good juicers and bad juicers. Unfortunately, you won't know if you have a bad juicer until you buy and use it. That's why I created this guide to buying the perfect juicer.

This chapter discusses the different types of juicers. We will also discuss the important factors to consider when buying a juicer. Ultimately, you will walk away with the knowledge you need to choose the perfect juicer. But first, let's start by addressing a very important question.

CAN I JUST USE A BLENDER TO JUICE FRUITS AND VEGETABLES?

Technically, you can use a blender to make juice. But it's much harder to use a blender to make juice. For example, you would have to strain the pulp from the juice. A juicer removes the pulp from the juice, so you don't have to.

Let's take a look at some important differences between juicing and blending:

1. **Texture:** Blending fruits and vegetables creates a thicker drink. It has a smoothie-like texture because it retains all of the fiber from the produce. On the other hand, juicing removes the liquid from fruits and vegetables, leaving behind fiber-rich pulp.
2. **Nutrient Concentration:** Juicing produces a concentrated source of vitamins, minerals, and antioxidants by removing fiber. This makes it easier for your body to absorb nutrients. Blending retains all of the fiber, which can slow down nutrient absorption. However, it also provides additional health benefits such as improved digestion and keeping you fuller longer.
3. **Ease of Digestion:** Juicing removes the fiber. This makes it easier for your body to digest and absorb the nutrients from fruits and vegetables. This can benefit individuals with digestive issues or those who have difficulty digesting fiber. Blended drinks may be more filling and may take longer to digest due to the fiber content.
4. **Convenience:** Juicing requires a juicer. Blending requires a blender. While this may seem convenient, it's not. Juicers are specifically designed to remove the juice from

produce efficiently and effectively. Blenders will not extract juice as efficiently and will leave behind more pulp.

5. **Versatility:** You can use a blender to make a wide variety of beverages, including smoothies, shakes, and purees. They can also blend several ingredients including whole fruits and vegetables, nuts, seeds, and liquids. Juicers are primarily designed for juicing fruits and vegetables and may not be as versatile for other recipes.

Ultimately, whether you choose to use a blender or a juicer depends on your personal preferences. Investing in a juicer may be worthwhile if you prefer the lighter texture and concentrated nutrients of juice. It's also helpful for detoxing the body, supporting weight loss, or if you are looking for a convenient way to increase your intake of fruits and vegetables. However, a blender may be a better investment if you want thicker drinks, additional fiber, or use it to make different drinks.

Now that we have discussed the difference between a blender and a juicer let's move on to the types of juicers.

TYPES OF JUICERS

There are several types of juicers available. For example, there are centrifugal, citrus, and steam juicers. Each juicer has its own pros and cons. So, let's discuss each type of juicer in depth so you can make the best choice.

CENTRIFUGAL JUICERS

Centrifugal juicers are high-speed juicers. They have spinning blades that extract juice from fruits and vegetables. They are generally more affordable and work well with most types of produce. However, they may not be the best at extracting juice from leafy greens. So, keep this in mind if you plan to juice a lot of greens.

MASTICATING JUICERS

Masticating juicers use a slow crushing and squeezing action to extract juice from produce. They are also known as cold press or slow juicers. These juicers are more efficient at extracting juice from leafy greens. Masticating juicers produce less heat, which helps preserve the nutrients in the juice. However, they tend to be more expensive. So, consider your budget before purchasing this type of juicer.

CITRUS JUICERS

As the name implies, citrus juicers are designed for juicing citrus fruits. You can juice oranges, grapefruits, lemons, and limes in this type of juicer. These juicers are typically affordable and easy to use. But you can only juice citrus fruits in this juicer. So, it may not be worthwhile if you want to juice other fruits or vegetables.

STEAM JUICERS

Steam juicers use steam to extract the juice from produce. They look like stainless steel double boilers. They can be used on the stove to create juice you can store in the fridge, freezer, or pantry. The juice is usually free of pulp. However, it loses some nutrients because of the steam. Steam juicers may be perfect if you grow a lot of food in your garden or buy food in bulk. Either way, steam juicers are affordable tools that will do the job.

TRITURATING JUICERS

Triturating juicers crush and grind fruits and vegetables into fine pieces using rotating twin blades. The gears separate the juice from the pulp, creating a glass of smooth juice with little to no pulp. These juicers are perfect for hearty vegetables like sweet potatoes and leafy greens. They also work with soft fruits like berries. However, they do cost more than other types of juicers. But if you are making juice several times a week, this may be a worthy investment.

JUICING COMPARISON GUIDE

Juicer	Pros	Cons	Who Is It Best For
Centrifugal	• Fast • Easy to use • Easy to clean and maintain • Lightweight • Inexpensive	• Produces a lot of noise • Has trouble juicing leafy greens • Does not produce a lot of juice	• Beginners • People who want to juice a lot of hard fruits and veggies like apples, carrots, and cucumbers
Masticating	• Versatile • Makes little to no noise • Produces a lot of juice • Less waste • Produces juice with more nutrients	• High-priced • Slow • Hard to clean	• Persons who want to produce as much juice as possible with as much nutrients as possible • Persons who want to juice a variety of fruits and vegetables

Citrus	• Inexpensive • Easy to clean and maintain • Easy to store	• Limited to juicing citrus fruits only	• For persons who only want to make citrus juice
Steam	• Versatile • Easy to clean and maintain • Inexpensive	• Takes longer to produce juice • Some nutrients are lost because of the heat	• Persons who want to juice large amounts of fruits and vegetables
Triturating	• Versatile • Makes little to no noise • The most efficient type of juicer	• The most expensive type of juicer • Weighs a lot • Slow	• Persons who plan to juice produce several times a week • Persons who plan to juice leafy greens or wheatgrass

FACTORS TO CONSIDER WHEN BUYING A JUICER

Choosing the perfect juicer is not as easy as it sounds. There are several factors you need to consider to make sure your juicer works for you and not against you. Here are the most important factors you should consider when buying a juicer:

1. **Feed Tube Size:** Feed tube size matters. For example, a juicer with a large feed tube is easier to use. You can chop the produce into large pieces and feed it through the juicer. However, if the juicer has a small feed tube, you have to chop the food into smaller pieces, which takes more time.

2. **Pulp Container:** Juicers have a pulp container inside or outside the machine. A juicer with an external pulp container lets you juice foods in bulk without stopping to remove the pulp. A juicer with an internal pulp container, forces you to stop to remove the pulp from the machine before you can juice more foods.

3. **Speeds:** Juicers with multiple speeds squeeze the most juice out of your produce. Juicers with slower speeds are best for soft foods like berries or grapes. High speeds are better for firm produce and vegetables like apples, celery, and carrots.

4. **Yield and Nutrient Retention:** Each type of juicer produces a different amount of juice and nutrients. For example, masticating juicers generally produce more juice. They also retain more nutrients compared to centrifugal juicers. Consider how much juice different juicers produce and how well they preserve the juice's nutrients before buying a juicer.

5. **Ease of Use and Maintenance:** Choose a juicer that is easy to use and clean. Look at the size of the feeding chute, the location of the pulp container, and how it is

assembled. Does it have a specialized brush to clean the extraction mechanism? Considering these factors will ensure your juicer is easy to use and maintain in the long run.

6. **Think About Noise Level:** Some juicers make a lot of noise. The noise can be quite annoying if you live in a shared living space or don't like loud noises. Look for juicers that make little to no sound if noise concerns you.

7. **Check Durability and Warranty:** Buy a juicer made from durable materials. Make sure it has a solid warranty to ensure it will last.

8. **Set a Budget:** Juicers come in a range of price points. So, determine your budget and prioritize the features that are most important to you. Remember, investing in a high-quality juicer can save you money in the long run. You won't have to look for replacement parts or take it to be repaired often.

9. **Read Reviews and Compare Models:** Take the time to look at different juicer models. Review the reviews and compare features to find the best juicer. Consider factors such as warranty, performance, reliability, customer service, and overall value for money before buying a juicer.

By considering these factors and taking the time to research and compare different juicer models, you can choose the perfect juicer that suits your needs.

You now have the information you need to buy the perfect juicer. We have discussed the difference between juicing and blending, the different types of juicers, and important factors to consider.

Remember to pay attention to important factors like the cost, feeding tube size, and how easy the juicer is to use. These factors will help you choose the best juicer.

Now it's time to move on. The next chapter will cover tips for juicing and things you should not do when juicing. So turn the page, and let's get started.

TIPS FOR JUICING

Juicing is a simple way to increase your nutrient intake. But mastering the art of juicing takes a bit of finesse. The process itself is easy. However, these tips and tricks can make your juicing journey easier.

This chapter gives you 21 tips and tricks to help you make delicious and nutritious juices with ease. From choosing the freshest produce to experimenting with flavor combinations, these tips ensure you get the perfect juice every time.

JUICING DO'S

Here are some tips to help you get the most out of your juicer:

1. **Use Fresh, High-Quality Produce:** Buy ripe, organic fruits and vegetables whenever possible. Your juice will have the best flavor. Fresh produce yields better-tasting juice with higher nutritional value.
2. **Wash Your Produce Thoroughly:** Wash your fruits and vegetables under cold running water. It will remove any dirt, bacteria, or pesticide residues from the produce before you juice it. Scrub firm produce like apples and carrots with a brush, and remove any bruised or damaged areas before you use them.
3. **Don't throw away the pulp:** You don't have to toss the pulp in the trash. It is a waste of food and money. Use the pulp. It's full of fiber. Plus, it's easy to incorporate into recipes. For example, you can use carrot pulp to make carrot cake or add it to bolognese sauce. You can use broccoli pulp to make broccoli cheese soup. You can also compost it and use it in your garden. The ways to use your pulp are endless. To store your pulp, place it in an airtight container. Place it in the fridge for 2-3 days or the freezer for up to 1-2 months until you are ready to use it.
4. **Mix and Match:** Experiment with different fruits, vegetables, and herbs to create unique flavors. The hard work has already been done for you since there are 87 juice recipes in this book. However, you can customize these recipes to suit your tastes. For example, you can balance the flavor of sweet fruits like strawberries or blueberries with leafy greens like kale.

5. **Prep Your Ingredients:** Chop fruits and vegetables into smaller pieces. They will fit easily into your juicer's feeding tube. Removing any seeds, pits, or tough stems will help prevent damage to your juicer and ensure smooth operation.

6. **Swap Your Greens:** Switch up your leafy greens. Greens like spinach, kale, and Swiss chard regularly contain oxalates. Oxalates can interfere with calcium absorption. So, use a variety of greens in your juices.

7. **Drink Your Juice Immediately:** Drink your juice as soon as possible. This minimizes nutrient loss and oxidation. Fresh juice is most nutritious when consumed immediately. However, you can store the juice in an airtight container in the fridge for up to 24 hours.

8. **Drink Juice On An Empty Stomach:** Drinking fresh juice on an empty stomach makes it easier to digest. You can drink your juice in the morning before breakfast or use it as a meal replacement for your breakfast. This will allow your body to absorb the nutrients faster without interference from other foods.

9. **Clean Your Juicer Immediately:** It's easy to tell yourself you will clean it later. The truth is you won't clean it for a few days. You must resist temptation and clean it right after you make your juice. Cleaning your juicer every time you use it prevents pulp and food residue from building up in your juicer. Pulp and food residue can harbor bacteria, which may make you sick. Furthermore, it can also make your juice taste weird. So clean your juicer right after you use it.

10. **Line The Pulp Basket:** Line the pulp basket with plastic wrap. It will make cleaning up easy. You won't have to scrub the pulp from the basket. Carefully remove the plastic wrap from the basket, making sure not to spill the pulp, and toss it in the trash.

11. **Stay Hydrated:** Yes, juicing keeps you hydrated. However, drinking a lot of water throughout the day is still important to stay hydrated. Drink 8 or more 8 oz. glasses of water daily, in addition to any juice you consume.

12. **Start Simple:** If you're new to juicing, keep it simple. Make recipes that have 5 or fewer ingredients. As you become more comfortable, you can experiment with more complex recipes.

13. **Adjust Sweetness:** If you find your juice too sweet or not sweet enough, adjust the sweetness. For example, you can add ingredients like apples, carrots, or beets. These give the juice a natural sweetness, which helps it taste better. You can also add a little lemon or a small piece of ginger for a tangy or spicy kick.

14. **Use Citrus:** Citrus fruits like lemons, limes, and oranges can add brightness and depth of flavor to your juices. Consider adding a squeeze of citrus juice or zest to balance out the flavors of other ingredients.

15. **Add Superfoods:** Boost the nutritional content of your juices by adding superfoods like chia seeds, flaxseeds, hemp seeds, spirulina, or wheatgrass powder. These nutrient-dense ingredients can provide additional health benefits and make your juices taste even better.

16. **Experiment with Temperature:** Fresh juice is typically enjoyed cold. But you can experiment with serving your juice at room temperature or even warmed up for a comforting treat. A glass of warm juice may come in handy during colder months.

17. **Juice in Batches:** To save time, juice in large batches. You can store the extra juice in airtight containers in the refrigerator for later use. Just be sure to consume it within 24 hours for the best quality and freshness.

18. **Add Ice Cubes:** If you prefer cold juice but don't want to dilute it with water, add 3-4 ice cubes to the glass before adding the juice. This will help chill the juice without diluting its flavor.

19. **Garnish Your Juice:** Garnish your juice with fresh herbs, citrus slices, or edible flowers. It will make the juice look more appetizing. More importantly, it will make the juice taste better.

20. **Stay Organized:** Keep your kitchen organized and stocked with fresh produce. It will make juicing more convenient and enjoyable. Designate a specific area of your kitchen for your juicer and accessories, and keep your ingredients neatly organized so they are easily accessible.

21. **Listen To Your Body:** Pay attention to how your body responds to different ingredients or combinations of fruits and vegetables. Everyone's taste preferences and nutritional needs are unique. So, listen to your body's cues and adjust your recipes accordingly.

By following these tips, you can make delicious and nutritious juices at home that support your health and well-being.

JUICING DON'TS

Juicing adds more fruits and vegetables to your diet. However, there are some juicing don'ts you should know about before you start juicing.

1. **Don't Overdo the Fruit:** Fruits are delicious. They add natural sweetness to juices. However, it is important not to overdo it, especially if you're watching your sugar intake. Too much fruit may spike your blood sugar levels. It may also cause you to gain weight. Add more vegetables than fruits in your juices, and use fruits sparingly

for flavor. Alternatively, you can gradually decrease the amount of fruits in your juices and replace them with vegetables over time.

2. **Don't Forget the Greens:** Leafy greens like spinach, kale, and Swiss chard are nutritional powerhouses. They make excellent additions to juices. They add essential nutrients like vitamins, minerals, and antioxidants to your juice without adding a lot of calories. So don't skimp on the greens! Experiment with different greens to find what you like best.

3. **Don't Ignore Food Safety:** Always practice food safety when juicing. Wash your fruits and vegetables thoroughly with cold water before juicing them. Clean your juicer after each use to prevent the growth of harmful bacteria.

4. **Don't Drink Too Much Juice at Once:** While fresh juice is nutritious, it's best to consume it in moderation. Drinking large quantities of juice in one sitting can cause spikes in blood sugar levels. It may contribute to digestive issues like bloating and gas. Drink juice in small to moderate amounts to a balanced diet.

5. **Don't Store Juice for Too Long:** Fresh juice is best when consumed immediately after juicing. This gives you the freshest flavor and the most nutrients. Remember, you can only store your juice in the fridge for 24 hours. But it's best to drink it as soon as possible for the freshest taste.

6. **Don't Neglect Variety:** Mix it up! Don't get stuck in a rut with the same juice recipes day after day. There are more than 70 recipes in this book. So, experiment with different fruits, vegetables, and herbs to keep things interesting.

7. **Don't Juice Dry Foods:** Stay away from foods that contain little to no water. For example, coconut, rice, or sugar cane are impossible to juice. They contain little to no water which makes juicing them useless.

8. **Don't Use Random Tools to Juice Foods:** Most juicers come with a plastic plunger to push food through the feeding tube. Do not use your hands, a spoon, or anything but the plunger to push food through your juicer. If you do, you could injure yourself or destroy your juicer. Use the plunger the juicer came with instead.

9. **Don't Focus Solely on Juicing:** Juicing can be a healthy addition to your diet. But it shouldn't replace whole fruits and vegetables altogether. Whole fruits and vegetables provide important dietary fiber that is missing from juice, so be sure to incorporate them into your diet as well.

Make the most of your juicing journey by keeping these juicing don'ts in mind. You will be able to enjoy delicious juice that heals your body.

We talked about juicing do's and don'ts. So, you are equipped with the tools you need to get started juicing. So, let's move on to the reason why you are here. In the coming sections, you will find 80 delicious recipes designed to help your body heal from arthritis, diarrhea, thyroid issues, and more. So, let's get juicing!

HYPERTENSION

- Blueberries contain powerful compounds which act as antioxidants. They help increase nitric oxide production, which may reduce blood pressure and arterial stiffness (Johnson et al., 2015).
- Pineapples contain antioxidants, phytochemicals, and compounds like bromelain that may help lower lipid levels. It can also reduce inflammation, improve blood vessel function, and lower cholesterol levels (Zuraini et al., 2021).
- Beets are rich in nitrate. Nitrate is converted into nitric oxide, which helps relax and dilate blood vessels. This can help improve blood flow and lowering blood pressure levels (Bahadoran et al., 2017).
- Pomegranates can reduce systolic blood pressure (Stowe, 2011).
- Mangoes contain potassium and magnesium. One study found blood pressure was reduced when participants supplemented anti-hypertensive medication with potassium (Binia et al., 2015). Magnesium helps regulate your blood pressure (Gröber et al., 2015). Since mangoes contain magnesium and potassium, drinking mango juice could help reduce blood pressure.
- Peaches are low in sodium. They are rich in magnesium and potassium, which are associated with reduced blood pressure levels.

BLUEBERRY PINEAPPLE JUICE

Prep Time: 10 minutes | **Total Time:** 10 minutes | **Serves:** 2

Nutrition Information (Serving Size: 1 glass of blueberry pineapple juice)

Calories: 107 kcal   **Carbohydrates:** 27.4g   **Fats:** 0.4g

Protein: 1.6g   **Sugar:** 19.9g   **Fiber:** 3.4g

Sodium: 8mg   **Cholesterol:** 0mg

Ingredients

- 1 cup pineapple, cut into chunks
- 1 cup blueberries
- 1/2-inch piece ginger

Instructions

1. Place the pineapples, blueberries, and ginger in your juicer and process them into juice.
2. Pour it into 2 glasses and serve immediately.

BEET POMEGRANATE JUICE

Prep Time: 10 minutes | **Total Time:** 10 minutes | **Serves:** 3

Nutrition Information (Serving Size: 1 glass of beet pomegranate juice)

Calories: 109 kcal   **Carbohydrates:** 22.6g   **Fats:** 1.5g

Protein: 2.3g   **Sugar:** 16.8g   **Fiber:** 4.8g

Sodium: 55mg   **Cholesterol:** 0mg

Ingredients

- 3 large pomegranates, cut into 1-inch pieces.
- 3 large lemons, rind removed, halved
- 2 small beets, cut into 1-inch pieces.
- 1-inch piece of ginger

Instructions

1. Place the pomegranate, lemons, beets, and ginger in your juicer and process them into juice.
2. Pour it into 2 glasses and serve immediately.

MANGO PEACH JUICE

Prep Time: 10 minutes | **Total Time:** 10 minutes | **Serves:** 3

Nutrition Information (Serving Size: 1 glass of mango peach juice)

Calories: 120 kcal	**Carbohydrates:** 29.9g	**Fats:** 0.2g
Protein: 2g	**Sugar:** 25.6g	**Fiber:** 5.3g
Sodium: 0mg	**Cholesterol:** 0mg	

Ingredients

- 1 large mango, peeled, pitted, cut into 1-inch pieces
- 2 medium oranges, peeled, halved
- 4 medium peaches, quartered, pits removed

Instructions

1. Place the mango, oranges, and peaches in your juicer and process them into juice.
2. Pour it into 2 glasses and serve immediately.

HIGH CHOLESTEROL

- Pineapples contain bromelain. Bromelain can reduce various markers associated with high cholesterol levels. It can decrease the levels of total cholesterol level, free cholesterol, triglycerides, and free fatty acids (Chen et al., 2023). All of these markers are indicators of elevated cholesterol levels in the body.
- Carrots are associated with lower cholesterol levels. Carrots are naturally low in saturated fat and cholesterol, making them a heart-healthy choice for individuals looking to manage their cholesterol levels.
- Leafy greens contain plant sterols. They have been shown to significantly decrease bad cholesterol levels (Trautwein et al., 2018).
- Spinach contains vitamin K. Recent research suggests that vitamin K may help regulate high levels of total cholesterol and bad cholesterol and low levels. One study found that giving vitamin K2 to rabbits with high cholesterol reduced their total cholesterol levels (Manna & Kalita, 2016).
- Apples contain bioactive compounds such as proanthocyanidins.
- These compounds have been shown to decrease serum cholesterol, increase good cholesterol, and prevent bad cholesterol from oxidizing (Koutsos et al., 2019).

PINEAPPLE CARROT JUICE

Prep Time: 10 minutes | **Total Time:** 10 minutes | **Serves:** 2

Nutrition Information (Serving Size: 1 glass of pineapple carrot juice)

Calories: 177 kcal

Carbohydrates: 44.8g

Fats: 0.4g

Protein: 2.6g

Sugar: 30.2g

Fiber: 7.7g

Sodium: 107mg

Cholesterol: 0mg

Ingredients

- 1 medium pineapple, cut into 1-inch pieces
- 1 orange, peeled, quartered
- 5 medium carrots, peeled
- 2 inches of fresh turmeric

Instructions

1. Place the pineapple, orange, carrots, and turmeric in your juicer and process them into juice.
2. Pour it into 2 glasses and serve immediately.

VEGGIE JUICE

Prep Time: 10 minutes | **Total Time:** 10 minutes | **Serves:** 2

Nutrition Information (Serving Size: 1 glass of veggie juice)

Calories: 82 kcal

Carbohydrates: 18.6g

Fats: 0.4g

Protein: 3.9g

Sugar: 8g

Fiber: 4.5g

Sodium: 114mg

Cholesterol: 0mg

Ingredients

- 2 medium tomatoes, roughly chopped
- 2 medium carrots, peeled
- 1 medium stalk celery
- 1/2 cup romaine, shredded
- 1/2 cup spinach
- 1/4 cup parsley leaves
- 1/2 bunch kale
- 1/2 medium beet, roughly chopped
- 1 clove garlic

Instructions

1. Place the tomatoes, carrots, celery, romaine, spinach, parsley, kale, beet, and garlic in your juicer and process them in juice.
2. Pour it into 2 glasses and serve immediately.

SPINACH APPLE JUICE

Prep Time: 10 minutes | **Total Time:** 10 minutes | **Serves:** 2

Nutrition Information (Serving Size: 1 glass of spinach apple juice)

Calories: 80 kcal	**Carbohydrates:** 20.4g	**Fats:** 0.4g
Protein: 4.1g	**Sugar:** 10.9g	**Fiber:** 6.9g
Sodium: 74mg	**Cholesterol:** 0mg	

Ingredients

- 1 medium stalk celery
- 1-inch of ginger
- 1 medium Granny Smith apple, cored, quartered
- 4 cups of spinach
- 1 lime, peeled, quartered
- 2/3 cups fresh cilantro
- 3 cups iceberg lettuce, roughly chopped

Instructions

1. Place the celery, ginger, apple, spinach, lime, cilantro, and lettuce in your juicer and process them into juice.
2. Pour it into 2 glasses and serve immediately.

GUT HEALTH

- Mint may reduce nausea and bloating, support digestion, and treat stomach problems (Silva, 2020).
- Pineapples are rich in protease. This compound can help improve problems with intestinal movement that occur after surgery. It can also help inflammation-induced ileus (a condition where the intestines temporarily stop working). It does this by reducing the overproduction of a molecule called inducible nitric oxide synthase in the colon, which is associated with intestinal dysfunction (Kostiuchenko et al., 2022).
- Strawberries contain many polyphenols. Recent research suggests that polyphenols can act like prebiotics. Studies show consuming foods or supplements rich in polyphenols can change the composition of the gut microbiota by reducing certain types of bacteria (Firmicutes) and increasing others (Bifidobacteria, Lactobacillus, and Verrucomicrobia), which are associated with improved gut health (Ezzat-Zadeh et al., 2021).
- Research shows that beets contain compounds such as pectic-oligosaccharides that can improve the composition and activity of the gut microbiota. They stimulate the growth of healthy bacteria and support the function of probiotics. Some compounds also encourage the production of beneficial substances like short-chain fatty acids, which contribute to overall health (de Oliveira et al., 2020).

MINTY FRESH GREEN JUICE

Prep Time: 10 minutes | **Total Time:** 10 minutes | **Serves:** 2

Nutrition Information (Serving Size: 1 glass of minty fresh green juice)

Calories: 100 kcal   **Carbohydrates:** 20.2g   **Fats:** 0.3g

Protein: 3.2g   **Sugar:** 11.9g   **Fiber:** 5.1g

Sodium: 24mg   **Cholesterol:** 0mg

Ingredients

- 2 large gala apples
- 2 medium English cucumbers
- 1/3 cup mint leaves
- 1 bunch kale
- 1 lime, peeled, quartered

Instructions

1. Place the apples, cucumbers, mint, kale, and lime in your juicer and process them into juice.
2. Pour it into 2 glasses and serve immediately.

PINEAPPLE PEAR JUICE

Prep Time: 10 minutes | **Total Time:** 10 minutes | **Serves:** 3

Nutrition Information (Serving Size: 1 glass of pineapple pear juice)

Calories: 145 kcal   **Carbohydrates:** 35.7g   **Fats:** 1.3g

Protein: 2.3g   **Sugar:** 23.3g   **Fiber:** 5.6g

Sodium: 10mg   **Cholesterol:** 0mg

Ingredients

- 2 cups fresh pineapple, cut into 1-inch chunks,
- 3 medium pears
- 1 medium English cucumber
- 1-inch fresh turmeric
- 1/4 cup fresh parsley leaves

Instructions

1. Place the pineapples, pears, cucumber, turmeric, and parsley in your juicer and process them into juice.
2. Pour it into 2 glasses and serve immediately.

STRAWBERRY BEET JUICE

Prep Time: 10 minutes | **Total Time:** 10 minutes | **Serves:** 3

Nutrition Information (Serving Size: 1 glass of strawberry beet juice)

Calories: 67 kcal   **Carbohydrates:** 16.1g   **Fats:** 0.5g

Protein: 2.1g   **Sugar:** 9.8g   **Fiber:** 4.6g

Sodium: 65mg   **Cholesterol:** 0mg

Ingredients

- 2 small beets, trimmed, quartered
- 1 cup strawberries, trimmed, halved
- 1 lemon, rind removed, quartered

Instructions

1. Place the beets, strawberries, and lemon in your juicer and process them into juice.
2. Pour it into 2 glasses and serve immediately.

SINUS

- Oranges contain vitamin C which can help fight off sinus infections quicker (Taneja & Qureshi, 2015).
- Apples and celery contain high levels of water. Water keeps you hydrated which may it easier for mucus secretions to drain from the sinuses.
- Spinach contains compounds like flavonoids and polyphenols. These compounds have anti-inflammatory properties, which may reduce inflammation in the sinus passages, easing congestion and discomfort.

ZESTY CARROT REFRESHER

Prep Time: 10 minutes | **Total Time:** 10 minutes | **Serves:** 2

Nutrition Information (Serving Size: 1 glass of zesty carrot refresher)

Calories: 131 kcal	**Carbohydrates:** 33.8g	**Fats:** 0.5g
Protein: 2.5g	**Sugar:** 20.7g	**Fiber:** 8.2g
Sodium: 103mg	**Cholesterol:** 0mg	

Ingredients

- 3 large carrots
- 2 medium lemons, rind removed, halved
- 2 medium oranges, rind removed, halved
- 1 medium radish, trimmed, halved
- 1 sprig of dill

Instructions

1. Place the carrots, lemons, oranges, radish, and dill in your juicer and process them in juice.
2. Pour it into 2 glasses and serve immediately.

APPLE CELERY JUICE

Prep Time: 10 minutes | **Total Time:** 10 minutes | **Serves:** 2

Nutrition Information (Serving Size: 1 glass of apple celery juice)

Calories: 139 kcal	**Carbohydrates:** 36.5g	**Fats:** 0.2g
Protein: 0.7g	**Sugar:** 26.9g	**Fiber:** 9.1g
Sodium: 77mg	**Cholesterol:** 0mg	

Ingredients

- 3 large stalks of celery, trimmed
- 1/2-inch piece of fresh ginger
- 3 medium Granny Smith apples, cored, quartered

Instructions

1. Place the celery, apples, and ginger in your juicer and process them into juice.
2. Pour it into 2 glasses and serve immediately.

SPINACH CUCUMBER JUICE

Prep Time: 10 minutes | **Total Time:** 10 minutes | **Serves:** 2

Nutrition Information (Serving Size: 1 glass of spinach cucumber juice)

Calories: 60 kcal   **Carbohydrates:** 13.6g   **Fats:** 0.1g

Protein: 4.5g   **Sugar:** 2.1g   **Fiber:** 5.9g

Sodium: 99mg   **Cholesterol:** 0mg

Ingredients

- 2 large English cucumbers, peeled and cut into long strips
- 2 limes, peeled, quartered
- 3 cups baby spinach

Instructions

1. Place the limes, cucumbers, and spinach in your juicer and process them into juice.
2. Pour it into 2 glasses and serve immediately.

CANCER

- Beets contain betalains. This compound may protect cells from damage, slowing down tumor growth, and encourage the death of cancerous cells (Chen et al., 2021).
- Carrots contain falcarinol and falcarindiol. These compounds have been shown to inhibit the growth of cancer cells and prevent cancer development in the large bowel in animal studies. More research is needed to see the effect of these compounds in humans (Deding et al., 2023).
- Eating green leafy vegetables is linked to a reduced risk of colon cancer (Smith et al., 2019). Green leafy vegetables contain lutein. This compound can reduce the risks of bladder, oral, and oesophageal cancer (Green Leafy Vegetable and Lutein Intake and Multiple Health Outcomes, 2021).
- Berries contain substances that help decrease inflammation in the body, which is linked to the development and progression of cancer. They can also inhibit blood vessel formation, protect DNA, and influence the behavior of cancer cells (Kristo et al., 2016).

BEET CARROT JUICE

Prep Time: 10 minutes | **Total Time:** 10 minutes | **Serves:** 2

Nutrition Information (Serving Size: 1 glass of beet carrot juice)

Calories: 117 kcal   **Carbohydrates:** 28.9g   **Fats:** 0.2g

Protein: 5.1g   **Sugar:** 11.7g   **Fiber:** 8g

Sodium: 312mg   **Cholesterol:** 0mg

Ingredients

- 5 medium carrots, peeled.
- 5 medium stalks of celery
- 1 medium beet, trimmed, quartered.
- 1 cup beet greens
- 1-inch piece of ginger

Instructions

1. Place the carrots, celery, beet, beet greens, and ginger in your juicer and process them in juice.
2. Pour it into 2 glasses and serve immediately.

LEAFY GREEN JUICE

Prep Time: 10 minutes | **Total Time:** 10 minutes | **Serves:** 2

Nutrition Information (Serving Size: 1 glass of leafy green juice)

Calories: 99 kcal   **Carbohydrates:** 22.6g   **Fats:** 0.4g

Protein: 4.4g   **Sugar:** 12.9g   **Fiber:** 6.6g

Sodium: 230mg   **Cholesterol:** 0mg

Ingredients

- 1 cup romaine lettuce, roughly chopped.
- 1/4 medium head of red cabbage, roughly chopped
- 1 medium Granny Smith apple, cored, quartered.
- 1/2 medium green bell pepper, roughly chopped.
- 1/4 cup watercress
- 3 Swiss chard leaves
- 1 cup beet greens

Instructions

1. Place the romaine lettuce, cabbage, apple, bell pepper, watercress, Swiss chard, and beet greens in your juicer and process them into juice.
2. Pour it into 2 glasses and serve immediately.

Notes: Choose 3 small inner Swiss chard leaves to reduce the bitter flavor.

BERRY LEMON CRUSH

Prep Time: 10 minutes | **Total Time:** 10 minutes | **Serves:** 2

Nutrition Information (Serving Size: 1 glass of berry lemon crush)

Calories: 99 kcal

Carbohydrates: 26.8g

Fats: 0.3g

Protein: 2.6g

Sugar: 14g

Fiber: 7.2g

Sodium: 39mg

Cholesterol: 0mg

Ingredients

- 3 lemons, peeled, quartered
- 1 cup whole cranberries
- 1 cup fresh blueberries
- 1 large carrot

Instructions

1. Place the oranges, cranberries, blueberries, and carrots in your juicer and process them into juice.
2. Pour it into 2 glasses and serve immediately.

DIABETES

- Spinach leaves are packed with nutrients like minerals, vitamins, and polyphenols. These compounds can help improve your blood sugar levels (Flores-Estrada et al., 2023). Therefore, spinach may help you manage diabetes and decrease your risk of complications related to diabetes.
- Strawberries can help reduce high blood sugar levels and excessive insulin production after meals in people who have trouble responding to insulin properly (Calvano et al., 2019).
- Tomatoes have a low glycemic index. Foods with a low GI are less likely to cause spikes in blood sugar, making them suitable choices for individuals with diabetes.
- Honeydew melons can be used to help treat or prevent diabetes (Khalid Mohammed Khan et al., 2023).

GRAPEFRUIT GREEN JUICE

Prep Time: 10 minutes | **Total Time:** 10 minutes | **Serves:** 3

Nutrition Information (Serving Size: 1 glass of grapefruit green juice)

Calories: 104 kcal	**Carbohydrates:** 24.8g	**Fats:** 0.3g
Protein: 4.6g	**Sugar:** 13.6g	**Fiber:** 5.6g
Sodium: 125mg	**Cholesterol:** 0mg	

Ingredients

- 2 cups spinach
- 1 cup pineapple, cut into 1-inch pieces.
- 1/2 cup fresh parsley leaves
- 2 medium celery stalks roughly chopped.
- 1 medium English cucumber, cut into 1-inch chunks.
- 1 medium grapefruit, peel removed, quartered.

Instructions

1. Place the spinach, pineapple, parsley, celery, cucumbers, and grapefruit in your juicer and process them into juice.
2. Pour it into 2 glasses and serve immediately.

STRAWBERRY TOMATO JUICE

Prep Time: 10 minutes | **Total Time:** 10 minutes | **Serves:** 3

Nutrition Information (Serving Size: 1 glass of strawberry tomato juice)

Calories: 81 kcal	**Carbohydrates:** 18.8g	**Fats:** 0.8g
Protein: 2.6g	**Sugar:** 12.2g	**Fiber:** 5.2g
Sodium: 10mg	**Cholesterol:** 0mg	

Ingredients

- 1 lb. strawberries, trimmed, halved.
- 2 large tomatoes, quartered

Instructions

1. Place the strawberries and tomatoes in a juicer and process them into juice.
2. Pour it into 2 glasses and serve immediately.

MELON LETTUCE JUICE

Prep Time: 10 minutes | **Total Time:** 10 minutes | **Serves:** 2

Nutrition Information (Serving Size: 1 glass of melon lettuce juice)

Calories: 51 kcal   **Carbohydrates:** 13.8g   **Fats:** 0.4g

Protein: 2.3g   **Sugar:** 1.9g   **Fiber:** 3.3g

Sodium: 66mg   **Cholesterol:** 0mg

Ingredients

- 2 cups iceberg lettuce, roughly chopped.
- 1 cup honeydew melon
- 1/2 cup fresh parsley leaves
- 2 medium celery stalks roughly chopped.
- 1 medium lemon, peel removed, quartered.

Instructions

1. Place the lettuce, honeydew melon, parsley, celery, and lemon in your juicer and process them into juice.
2. Pour it into 2 glasses and serve immediately.

KIDNEY DISEASE

- Grapes are rich in antioxidants. They may help prevent the development of chronic kidney disease (Zhu & Du, 2019).
- Pears are low in sodium, which may help prevent kidney disease. Research shows pears contain high levels of malic acid, which can protect you from getting kidney stones (Manfredini et al., 2016).
- Cherries are low in phosphorous and sodium. If [people with kidney disease eat large amounts of these nutrients, it can increase the risk of cardiovascular complications and death (Vervloet et al., 2016).
- Lime juice contains high concentrations of citrate, a compound that may help reduce the risk of developing kidney stones (Siener, 2021).
- Apples contain low levels of potassium, phosphorus, and sodium. They are a great choice for kidney-friendly juices.

GRAPE PEAR JUICE

Prep Time: 10 minutes | **Total Time:** 10 minutes | **Serves:** 2

Nutrition Information (Serving Size: 1 glass of grape pear juice)

Calories: 150 kcal	**Carbohydrates:** 37.3g	**Fats:** 1.1g
Protein: 1.8g	**Sugar:** 25g	**Fiber:** 4.5g
Sodium: 1mg	**Cholesterol:** 0mg	

Ingredients

- 1 cup red grapes
- 1/2 cup green grapes
- 1 medium pear, cored, quartered
- 1 medium plum, pitted quartered
- 1 lemon, peeled, quartered

Instructions

1. Place the grapes, pear, plum, and lemon in your juicer and process them into juice.
2. Pour it into 2 glasses and serve immediately.

CHERRY LIME JUICE

Prep Time: 10 minutes | **Total Time:** 10 minutes | **Serves:** 2

Nutrition Information (Serving Size: 1 glass of cherry lime juice)

Calories: 117 kcal	**Carbohydrates:** 30.1g	**Fats:** 0.5g
Protein: 2.4g	**Sugar:** 17.2g	**Fiber:** 6.1g
Sodium: 34mg	**Cholesterol:** 0mg	

Ingredients

- 1 cup pitted cherries
- 2 limes, peeled, halved
- 1 medium Granny Smith apple
- 1/2 medium English cucumber
- 1 small beet, trimmed, quartered
- 1-inch ginger

Instructions

1. Place the cherries, limes, apple, cucumber, and beet in your juicer and process them into juice.
2. Pour it into 2 glasses and serve immediately.

APPLE PEAR JUICE

Prep Time: 10 minutes | **Total Time:** 10 minutes | **Serves:** 2

Nutrition Information (Serving Size: 1 glass of apple pear juice)

Calories: 224 kcal   **Carbohydrates:** 56.4g   **Fats:** 1.2g

Protein: 2.7g   **Sugar:** 36g   **Fiber:** 10.9g

Sodium: 64mg   **Cholesterol:** 0mg

Ingredients

- 2 medium Granny Smith apples, cored, quartered
- 2 medium pears, cored, quartered
- 3 medium carrots
- 2 lemons, peeled, quartered

Instructions

1. Place the apples, pears, carrots, and lemons in your juicer and process them into juice.
2. Pour it into 2 glasses and serve immediately.

COLDS/FLU

- Ginger helps people with chronic respiratory problems like coughs and colds by clearing mucus from their lungs, helping them breathe better and recover faster. It also soothes a sore throat by reducing inflammation and easing discomfort (Bhadra et al., 2021).
- Oranges are rich in vitamins and minerals. They contain high levels of vitamin C. It is an antioxidant that helps boost your body's immune system.
- Beets are rich in nitric oxide. It acts as a natural defense against germs, like viruses and bacteria (Ritz et al., 2019). Therefore, beet juice can strengthen our immune system's ability to fight off colds or other infections.
- Pomegranates are rich in vitamin C, which can support the immune system. Vitamin C helps strengthen the body's natural defenses and may reduce the severity and duration of cold symptoms. It also contains powerful antioxidants, which help fight oxidative stress and inflammation in the body (Khan et al., 2020). These antioxidants may help reduce inflammation in the respiratory tract and alleviate symptoms like coughing and congestion associated with colds.

COLD/FLU KICKER

Prep Time: 10 minutes | **Total Time:** 10 minutes | **Serves:** 2

Nutrition Information (Serving Size: 1 glass of citrus kicker juice)

Calories: 296 kcal	**Carbohydrates:** 74g	**Fats:** 0.9g
Protein: 3.8g	**Sugar:** 52.3g	**Fiber:** 16.4g
Sodium: 129mg	**Cholesterol:** 0mg	

Ingredients

- 4 oranges, peel removed, quartered
- 1 lemon, peel removed, quartered
- 2 inch piece of ginger
- 1 inch piece of turmeric
- 5 large carrots
- 2 medium Granny Smith apples

Instructions

1. Place the oranges, lemon, ginger, turmeric, carrots, and apples in your juicer and process them into juice.
2. Pour it into 2 glasses and serve immediately.

BEET BOOSTER JUICE

Prep Time: 10 minutes | **Total Time:** 10 minutes | **Serves:** 3

Nutrition Information (Serving Size: 1 glass of beet booster juice)

Calories: 237 kcal	**Carbohydrates:** 59.3g	**Fats:** 0.2g
Protein: 3.8g	**Sugar:** 38.6g	**Fiber:** 10.6g
Sodium: 178mg	**Cholesterol:** 0mg	

Ingredients

- 4 medium beets, quartered
- 6 medium carrots, peeled
- 1/2 medium red onion, roughly chopped
- 3 medium red delicious apples, cored, quartered
- 2 cups pineapple, cut into 1-inch chunks

Instructions

1. Place the beets, carrots, apples, red onions, and pineapples in your juicer and process them into juice.
2. Pour it into 2 glasses and serve immediately.

POMEGRANATE KALE JUICE

Prep Time: 10 minutes | **Total Time:** 10 minutes | **Serves:** 2

Nutrition Information (Serving Size: 1 glass of pomegranate kale juice)

Calories: 154 kcal   **Carbohydrates:** 37.9g   **Fats:** 0.7g

Protein: 4.8g   **Sugar:** 23.3g   **Fiber:** 4.9g

Sodium: 36mg   **Cholesterol:** 0mg

Ingredients

- 1 bunch kale
- 2 medium pomegranates

- 1 lemon, peeled, quartered
- 2 medium grapefruits, peeled, quartered

Instructions

1. Place the kale, pomegranates, lemon, and grapefruits in your juicer and process them into juice.
2. Pour it into 2 glasses and serve immediately.

EPILEPSY

- Swiss chard contains magnesium. Studies show taking vitamin E regularly can be helpful for epilepsy, especially in persons whose seizures are difficult to control with standard medications. This suggests that vitamin E could be a useful additional treatment option for epilepsy (Kim & Cho, 2019).
- Brussel sprouts and broccoli contain vitamin C. Animal studies suggest vitamin C may help reduce seizures in epilepsy by reducing oxidative stress. However, more research is needed to understand its effectiveness better (Kim & Cho, 2019).

SWISS CHARD ENERGY JUICE

Prep Time: 10 minutes | **Total Time:** 10 minutes | **Serves:** 2

Nutrition Information (Serving Size: 1 glass of Swiss chard energy juice)

Calories: 161 kcal	**Carbohydrates:** 37.2g	**Fats:** 0.5g
Protein: 5.5g	**Sugar:** 20.9g	**Fiber:** 6.6g
Sodium: 145mg	**Cholesterol:** 0mg	

Ingredients

- 2 bunches of kale
- 1 bunch of Swiss chard
- 1 stalk of broccoli
- 3 medium stalks of celery
- 1 cup green grapes
- 1 cup cherry tomatoes
- 1 medium orange peeled, quartered
- 1/2-inch piece of ginger

Instructions

1. Place the kale, Swiss chard, celery, grapes, cherry tomatoes, orange, and ginger in your juicer and process them in juice.
2. Pour it into 2 glasses and serve immediately.

BRUSSEL SPROUT CLEANSER

Prep Time: 10 minutes | **Total Time:** 10 minutes | **Serves:** 2

Nutrition Information (Serving Size: 1 glass of Brussel sprout cleanser)

Calories: 65 kcal	**Carbohydrates:** 13.5g	**Fats:** 0.6g
Protein: 5.3g	**Sugar:** 3.2g	**Fiber:** 5.6g
Sodium: 61mg	**Cholesterol:** 0mg	

Ingredients

- 2 cups Brussels sprouts
- 1 stalk of broccoli
- 2 cups of spinach
- 1/2 lemon, peeled

Instructions

1. Place the Brussel sprouts, broccoli, spinach, and lemon in your juicer and process them into juice.
2. Pour it into 2 glasses and serve immediately.

BROCCOLI JUICE

Prep Time: 10 minutes | **Total Time:** 10 minutes | **Serves:** 2

Nutrition Information (Serving Size: 1 glass of Broccoli juice)

Calories: 73 kcal	**Carbohydrates:** 17.4g	**Fats:** 0.8g
Protein: 2.4g	**Sugar:** 9.7g	**Fiber:** 3.9g
Sodium: 27mg	**Cholesterol:** 0mg	

Ingredients

- 1 cup broccoli
- 1 cup spinach
- 1 medium pear
- 1/2 lemon, peeled
- 8 leaves mint

Instructions

1. Place the broccoli, spinach, pear, lemon, and mint in your juicer and process them into juice.
2. Pour it into 2 glasses and serve immediately.

BRONCHITIS

- Broccoli contains sulforaphane. It can activate a protein called Nrf2, which can help reduce oxidative stress and enhance the ability of immune cells called macrophages to clear bacteria from the lungs (Wise et al., 2016). Consuming broccoli may help alleviate symptoms and improve outcomes in conditions like bronchitis.
- Celery contains compounds like apigenin and luteolin, which have anti-inflammatory properties (Salehi et al., 2019). In bronchitis, inflammation in the airways can lead to symptoms like coughing and difficulty breathing. Consuming celery may help reduce inflammation and ease symptoms.
- Lemons contain high levels of vitamin C, which can support the immune system and help you manage symptoms of bronchitis like a cough or fever (Sadikan et al., 2023).
- Ginger can help clear mucus from the lungs and suppress coughing, which can ease symptoms of bronchitis, coughs, and colds (Wardani et al., 2023).
- Elderberries support respiratory health by boosting the immune system and reducing inflammation, which can help alleviate bronchitis symptoms (Mahboubi, 2020).

BROCCOLI CELERY JUICE

Prep Time: 10 minutes | **Total Time:** 10 minutes | **Serves:** 2

Nutrition Information (Serving Size: 1 glass of broccoli celery juice)

Calories: 83 kcal	**Carbohydrates:** 20g	**Fats:** 0.3g
Protein: 2.3g	**Sugar:** 12.5g	**Fiber:** 5.5g
Sodium: 65mg	**Cholesterol:** 0mg	

Ingredients

- 3 medium stalks of celery
- 1/2 medium red onion, roughly chopped
- 1 clove of garlic
- 1 stalk of broccoli, roughly chopped
- 1 medium Golden delicious apple

Instructions

1. Place the celery, red onion, garlic, broccoli, and apple in your juicer and process them into juice.
2. Pour it into 2 glasses and serve immediately.

LEMON TURMERIC GINGER SHOT

Prep Time: 10 minutes | **Total Time:** 10 minutes | **Serves:** 4

Nutrition Information (Serving Size: 1 lemon turmeric ginger shot)

Calories: 41 kcal	**Carbohydrates:** 9.3g	**Fats:** 0.4g
Protein: 0.8g	**Sugar:** 7g	**Fiber:** 1.9g
Sodium: 5mg	**Cholesterol:** 0mg	

Ingredients

- 2 inches of turmeric
- 2 inches of fresh ginger
- 2 lemons, peel removed, quartered
- 2 medium oranges, peel removed, quartered

Instructions

1. Place the turmeric, ginger, lemons, and oranges in your juicer and process them in juice.
2. Pour it into 2 glasses and serve immediately.

ELDERBERRY PEAR JUICE

Prep Time: 10 minutes | **Total Time:** 10 minutes | **Serves:** 2

Nutrition Information (Serving Size: 1 glass of elderberry pear juice)

Calories: 188 kcal   **Carbohydrates:** 47.2g   **Fats:** 1.3g

Protein: 2.2g   **Sugar:** 21.4g   **Fiber:** 12.4g

Sodium: 6mg   **Cholesterol:** 0mg

Ingredients

- 2 lbs. elderberries
- 2 inches of fresh turmeric
- 1 medium pear
- 2 medium oranges, peel removed, quartered

Instructions

1. Place the elderberries, turmeric, pear, and oranges in your juicer and process them in juice.
2. Pour it into 2 glasses and serve immediately.

VISION PROBLEMS

- Green leafy vegetables like celery and cabbage may lower the risk of persons with glaucoma of developing glaucoma-related vision loss (Kang et al., 2016). However, more research is needed to confirm these findings and understand the protective effects of green leafy vegetables against glaucoma.
- Bell peppers contain lutein and zeaxanthin. These compounds may help reduce the risk of developing age-related macular degeneration (AMD), a leading cause of vision loss, and help maintain eye health (Mrowicka et al., 2022).
- Beets also contain lutein. It supports eye health and helps reduce the risk of optic conditions like age-related macular degeneration and cataracts (Mrowicka et al., 2022).
- Parsley's nutrients and antioxidants could support optical health by reducing the risk of vision problems such as cataracts and age-related macular degeneration (Sarwar et al., 2016).

GLAUCOMA BUSTER

Prep Time: 10 minutes | **Total Time:** 10 minutes | **Serves:** 2

Nutrition Information (Serving Size: 1 glass of glaucoma buster)

Calories: 58 kcal	**Carbohydrates:** 12.9g	**Fats:** 0.3g
Protein: 2.6g	**Sugar:** 6.4g	**Fiber:** 5.2g
Sodium: 103mg	**Cholesterol:** 0mg	

Ingredients

- 3 stalks of celery
- 1/4 medium head of cabbage
- 1 medium radish
- 1/2 cup fresh parsley
- 1 large carrot, peeled

Instructions

1. Place the celery, cabbage, radish, parsley, and carrot in your juicer and process them into juice.
2. Pour it into 2 glasses and serve immediately.

MACULAR DEGENERATION KICKER

Prep Time: 10 minutes | **Total Time:** 10 minutes | **Serves:** 2

Nutrition Information (Serving Size: 1 glass of macular degeneration kicker)

Calories: 155 kcal	**Carbohydrates:** 38.8g	**Fats:** 0.8g
Protein: 3.3g	**Sugar:** 22.9g	**Fiber:** 11.9g
Sodium: 40mg	**Cholesterol:** 0mg	

Ingredients

- 1 medium red bell pepper, roughly chopped
- 1 medium green bell pepper, roughly chopped
- 1 cup raspberries
- 1 bunch kale
- 2 medium gala apples

Instructions

1. Place the bell peppers, raspberries, kale, and apples in your juicer and process them into juice.
2. Pour it into 2 glasses and serve immediately.

OPTICAL BOOSTER

Prep Time: 10 minutes | **Total Time:** 10 minutes | **Serves:** 2

Nutrition Information (Serving Size: 1 glass of optical booster)

Calories: 146 kcal   **Carbohydrates:** 32.2g   **Fats:** 0.9g

Protein: 7.1g   **Sugar:** 13.9g   **Fiber:** 14.7g

Sodium: 207mg   **Cholesterol:** 0mg

Ingredients

- 2 medium beets, trimmed, quartered
- 1/4 medium head of red cabbage
- 1 head of endive lettuce
- 1/2 cup parsley
- 2 large carrots, peeled

Instructions

1. Place the beets, cabbage, endive, parsley, and carrot in your juicer and process them into juice.
2. Pour it into 2 glasses and serve immediately.

GOUT

- Cherries contain antioxidants and anti-inflammatory properties that can help reduce inflammation. They may help ease the sudden pain of gout attacks and the long-term joint damage caused by the condition (Collins et al., 2019).
- Cucumbers can relieve pain caused by gout by lowering uric acid levels (Akhtar et al., (2020).
- Watermelon can help lower uric acid levels in the body. Reducing uric acid provides relief from gout symptoms and helps prevent gout attacks (Nadeem et al., 2022).
- Kale's nutrient-rich composition, including vitamins, minerals, and antioxidants, may help alleviate symptoms of gout and prevent gout attacks (Hafez et al., 2017).
- Oranges contain high levels of vitamin C, which is linked to decreased uric acid levels and a reduced risk of gout. Therefore, consuming oranges may help prevent gout or alleviate its symptoms (Nakagawa et al., 2019).

CUCUMBER CHERRY JUICE

Prep Time: 10 minutes | **Total Time:** 10 minutes | **Serves:** 2

Nutrition Information (Serving Size: 1 glass of cucumber cherry juice)

Calories: 65 kcal   **Carbohydrates:** 15.6g   **Fats:** 0.1g

Protein: 2.6g   **Sugar:** 10.3g   **Fiber:** 3.1g

Sodium: 53mg   **Cholesterol:** 0mg

Ingredients

- 1 medium English cucumber, roughly chopped
- 2 medium stalks of celery, rinsed,
- 1/2 of a lemon, peel removed
- 1 -inch of ginger
- 1 cup fresh cherries, pitted

Instructions

1. Place the cucumbers, celery, lemon, ginger, and cherries in your juicer and process them into juice.
2. Pour it into 2 glasses and serve immediately.

WATERMELON CHERRY JUICE

Prep Time: 10 minutes | **Total Time:** 10 minutes | **Serves:** 2

Nutrition Information (Serving Size: 1 glass of watermelon cherry juice)

Calories: 215 kcal   **Carbohydrates:** 49g   **Fats:** 0.6g

Protein: 3g   **Sugar:** 44g   **Fiber:** 5g

Sodium: 53mg   **Cholesterol:** 0mg

Ingredients

- 2 cups watermelon
- 1 ½ cups raspberries
- 2 cups pitted cherries

Instructions

1. Place the watermelon, raspberries, and cherries in your juicer and process them in juice.
2. Pour it into 2 glasses and serve immediately.

KALE ORANGE BLASTER

Prep Time: 10 minutes | **Total Time:** 10 minutes | **Serves:** 2

Nutrition Information (Serving Size: 1 glass of kale orange blaster)

Calories: 122 kcal	**Carbohydrates:** 19.3g	**Fats:** 0.9g
Protein: 4.2g	**Sugar:** 13.3g	**Fiber:** 5.9g
Sodium: 46mg	**Cholesterol:** 0mg	

Ingredients

- 2 bunches of kale
- 2 medium oranges, peeled, quartered
- 1/2 lemon, peeled
- 1-inch of ginger

Instructions

1. Place the kale, oranges, lemon, and ginger in your juicer and process them in juice.
2. Pour it into 2 glasses and serve immediately.

HEADACHE

- Beet greens contain compounds that may help decrease inflammation and oxidative stress in the body, which are factors often associated with headaches. Therefore, incorporating beet greens into the diet may offer natural relief from headaches (Mirzababaei et al., 2018).
- Cucumbers contain bioactive substances that may help alleviate headaches by reducing inflammation and providing a cooling sensation when consumed (Sahu & Sahu, 2015).
- Celery contains bioactive compounds that may help alleviate headaches by reducing inflammation. These compounds can also act as mild diuretics, which could help decrease pressure in the head (Hussain et al., 2023).
- Ginger contains compounds that may help alleviate headaches. These compounds can reduce inflammation and block pain signals in the brain (Bijan Helli et al., 2022).

HEADACHE AWAY

Prep Time: 10 minutes | **Total Time:** 10 minutes | **Serves:** 2

Nutrition Information (Serving Size: 1 glass of headache away)

Calories: 89 kcal

Carbohydrates: 22g

Fats: 0.5g

Protein: 5g

Sugar: 8.4g

Fiber: 6.7g

Sodium: 175mg

Cholesterol: 0mg

Ingredients

- 1 cup pineapple, cut into chunks
- 2 beet green leaves
- 1/2 cup spinach
- 2 medium stalks of celery
- 1 medium cucumber
- 1 lemon, peeled, quartered
- 1-inch turmeric root

Instructions

1. Place the pineapple, beet greens, spinach, celery, cucumber, lemon, and turmeric in your juicer and process them into juice.
2. Pour it into 2 glasses and serve immediately.

MIGRAINE RELIEVER

Prep Time: 10 minutes | **Total Time:** 10 minutes | **Serves:** 2

Nutrition Information (Serving Size: 1 glass of migraine reliever)

Calories: 110 kcal

Carbohydrates: 16.1g

Fats: 0.8g

Protein: 3g

Sugar: 16.1g

Fiber: 4.4g

Sodium: 49mg

Cholesterol: 0mg

Ingredients

- 2 cups alfalfa sprouts
- 1 bunch kale
- 2 stalks medium stalks celery
- 2 medium gala apples
- 1-inch piece ginger
- 1/2 lemon, peeled

Instructions

1. Place the alfalfa sprouts, kale, celery, ginger, and lemon in your juicer and process them into juice.
2. Pour it into 2 glasses and serve immediately.

SOOTHING PINE BEET JUICE

Prep Time: 10 minutes | **Total Time:** 10 minutes | **Serves:** 2

Nutrition Information (Serving Size: 1 glass of soothing pine beet juice)

Calories: 112 kcal	**Carbohydrates:** 26.9g	**Fats:** 0.2g
Protein: 3.7g	**Sugar:** 19.7g	**Fiber:** 4.6g
Sodium: 132mg	**Cholesterol:** 0mg	

Ingredients

- 1 medium pineapple, peeled, roughly chopped
- 4 medium beets
- 1-inch ginger
- 1 lemon, peeled, quartered

Instructions

1. Place the pineapples, beets, ginger, and lemon in your juicer and process them into juice.
2. Pour it into 2 glasses and serve immediately.

ECZEMA

- Beets contain compounds that may help dilate blood vessels, improve circulation, and reduce inflammation, which are factors often associated with headaches (Kukadia et al., 2019).
- Spinach contains quercetin, a compound known for its anti-inflammatory effects, which may help alleviate eczema symptoms by reducing skin inflammation (Mlcek et al., 2016).
- Berries contain resveratrol. This compound contains anti-inflammatory and antioxidant effects. These properties may help alleviate symptoms of eczema, as inflammation and oxidative stress are often involved in the condition (Salvo et al., 2023).
- Celery contains compounds that might help reduce inflammation in the body, which could be beneficial for conditions like eczema (Kooti & Daraei, 2017).

SPINACH KALE JUICE

Prep Time: 10 minutes | **Total Time:** 10 minutes | **Serves:** 2

Nutrition Information (Serving Size: 1 glass of spinach kale juice)

Calories: 127 kcal   **Carbohydrates:** 31.5g   **Fats:** 0.1g

Protein: 3.4g   **Sugar:** 17.9g   **Fiber:** 7.3g

Sodium: 53mg   **Cholesterol:** 0mg

Ingredients

- 2 cups spinach
- 2 bunches of kale
- 1 medium English cucumber
- 2 medium Golden delicious apples

Instructions

1. Place the spinach, kale, cucumber, and apples in your juicer and process them in juice.
2. Pour it into 2 glasses and serve immediately.

BERRY BLAST

Prep Time: 10 minutes | **Total Time:** 10 minutes | **Serves:** 2

Nutrition Information (Serving Size: 1 glass of berry blast)

Calories: 196 kcal   **Carbohydrates:** 50.9g   **Fats:** 0.7g

Protein: 2.4g   **Sugar:** 35.5g   **Fiber:** 14.2g

Sodium: 2mg   **Cholesterol:** 0mg

Ingredients

- 1 cup raspberries
- 1 cup blueberries
- 1 cup strawberries, trimmed, halved
- 1 cup blackberries
- 2 medium Granny Smith apples

Instructions

1. Place the raspberries, blueberries, strawberries, blackberries, and apples in your juicer and process them into juice.
2. Pour it into 2 glasses and serve immediately.

CELERY GRAPEFRUIT JUICE

Prep Time: 10 minutes | **Total Time:** 10 minutes | **Serves:** 2

Nutrition Information (Serving Size: 1 glass of celery grapefruit juice)

Calories: 105 kcal

Carbohydrates: 28g

Fats: 0g

Protein: 0.5g

Sugar: 15g

Fiber: 13g

Sodium: 575mg

Cholesterol: 0mg

Ingredients

- 2 bunches of celery
- 1 large pink grapefruit, peeled, quartered

Instructions

1. Place the celery and grapefruit in your juicer and process them into juice.
2. Pour it into 2 glasses and serve immediately.

ACID REFLUX

- Animal studies suggest a substance found in fennel oil might help speed up the digestion process in the stomach, which could benefit conditions like acid reflux. However, more research is needed to understand how fennel might affect acid reflux (Schulz et al., 2022).
- Apples are alkaline. They may help reduce the production of stomach acid, which can help decrease the frequency and severity of symptoms associated with acid reflux (Herdiana, 2023).
- Guava contains compounds that may help reduce the production of stomach acid and soothe the digestive system, which can help alleviate symptoms of acid reflux (Daswani et al., 2017).
- Cantaloupe is alkaline in nature. It can help neutralize stomach acid. Additionally, cantaloupe is low in acidity, which reduces the risk of triggering reflux symptoms.
- Sweet potatoes contain vitamins, minerals, and fiber, which can help support digestion and soothe the stomach lining. Additionally, their low acidity may make them easier on the digestive system, reducing the risk of triggering reflux symptoms. However, more research is needed to fully understand the effects of sweet potatoes on acid reflux (Eissa et al., 2021).
- Carrots contain secondary metabolites. These compounds have antioxidant and anti-inflammatory effects. They may help alleviate symptoms of conditions like acid reflux (Prasad et al., 2016).

FENNEL APPLE JUICE

Prep Time: 10 minutes | **Total Time:** 10 minutes | **Serves:** 2

Nutrition Information (Serving Size: 1 glass of fennel apple juice)

Calories: 184 kcal | **Carbohydrates:** 37.2g | **Fats:** 3.8g

Protein: 3.2g | **Sugar:** 17.4g | **Fiber:** 9.7g

Sodium: 312mg | **Cholesterol:** 0mg

Ingredients

- 2 medium Granny Smith apple, cored, quartered
- 2 large carrots, peeled
- 1 medium celery stalk
- 1 bulb fennel, roughly chopped
- 1-inch fresh ginger
- 1 lime, peeled, quartered

Instructions

1. Place the apples, carrots, celery, fennel, ginger, and lime in your juicer and process them into juice.
2. Pour it into 2 glasses and serve immediately.

GUAVA MELON JUICE

Prep Time: 10 minutes | **Total Time:** 10 minutes | **Serves:** 2

Nutrition Information (Serving Size: 1 glass of guava melon juice)

Calories: 75 kcal | **Carbohydrates:** 16.1g | **Fats:** 0.6g

Protein: 2.6g | **Sugar:** 10.6g | **Fiber:** 5.1g

Sodium: 27mg | **Cholesterol:** 0mg

Ingredients

- 1 medium cantaloupe, peeled, cut into 1-inch pieces
- 2 medium guavas, quartered
- 1 bunch kale
- 1-inch ginger

Instructions

1. Place the cantaloupe, guavas, kale, and ginger in your juicer and process them into juice.
2. Pour it into 2 glasses and serve immediately.

SWEET POTATO CARROT JUICE

Prep Time: 10 minutes | **Total Time:** 10 minutes | **Serves:** 2

Nutrition Information (Serving Size: 1 glass of sweet potato carrot juice)

Calories: 73 kcal   **Carbohydrates:** 17.6g   **Fats:** 0.1g

Protein: 1.7g   **Sugar:** 8.8g   **Fiber:** 4.2g

Sodium: 53mg   **Cholesterol:** 0mg

Ingredients

- 3 large carrots, peeled
- 1/2 orange sweet potato, scrubbed, cut into 1-inch pieces
- 1 medium Granny Smith apple, cored, quartered
- 1/2 medium English cucumber
- 1/4 medium head cabbage, roughly chopped
- 1-inch piece ginger

Instructions

1. Place the carrots, sweet potatoes, apple, cucumber, cabbage, and ginger in your juicer and process them into juice.
2. Pour it into 2 glasses and serve immediately.

HALITOSIS

- Mint contains compounds that can freshen breath by decreasing the odor-causing bacteria in the mouth and providing a pleasant scent (Khan et al., 2023).
- Fennel contains natural compounds that can freshen your breath. They can reduce the growth of bacteria in the mouth and mask unpleasant odors (Yadav Akshay et al., 2020).
- Cilantro contains compounds that can help reduce the growth of bacteria in the mouth. These bacteria are often responsible for causing bad breath (Shankar et al., 2022).
- Ginger contains compounds that can help slow the growth of bacteria responsible for bad breath in the mouth (Mamgain et al., 2016).

MINTY FRESH JUICE

Prep Time: 10 minutes | **Total Time:** 10 minutes | **Serves:** 2

Nutrition Information (Serving Size: 1 glass of minty fresh juice)

Calories: 142 kcal	**Carbohydrates:** 33.3g	**Fats:** 0.4g
Protein: 3g	**Sugar:** 21.4g	**Fiber:** 9.1g
Sodium: 15mg	**Cholesterol:** 0mg	

Ingredients

- 6 Granny Smith apples
- 1 medium English cucumber
- 2 cups of mint leaves
- 1 lemon, peeled, quartered

Instructions

1. Place the apples, cucumber, mint, and lemon in your juicer and process them into juice.
2. Pour it into 2 glasses and serve immediately.

BAD BREATH FIGHTER

Prep Time: 10 minutes | **Total Time:** 10 minutes | **Serves:** 2

Nutrition Information (Serving Size: 1 glass of bad breath fighter)

Calories: 77 kcal	**Carbohydrates:** 17.8g	**Fats:** 0.5g
Protein: 4.1g	**Sugar:** 1.2g	**Fiber:** 7.1g
Sodium: 83mg	**Cholesterol:** 0mg	

Ingredients

- 1 medium English cucumber, roughly chopped
- 1 cup of kale
- 1/2 cup mint leaves
- 1 lemon, peeled, quartered
- 1 medium fennel bulb, roughly chopped

Instructions

1. Place the cucumber, kale, mint, lemon, and fennel in your juicer and process them into juice.
2. Pour it into 2 glasses and serve immediately.

BREATH FRESHENER

Prep Time: 10 minutes | **Total Time:** 10 minutes | **Serves:** 2

Nutrition Information (Serving Size: 1 glass of breath freshener)

Calories: 121 kcal | **Carbohydrates:** 31.7g | **Fats:** 0.1g

Protein: 2.8g | **Sugar:** 20.7g | **Fiber:** 8.5g

Sodium: 1mg | **Cholesterol:** 0mg

Ingredients

- 2 medium gala apples
- 1/2 cup cilantro
- 1 lime, peeled

- 1 medium English cucumber
- 1-inch piece ginger
- 2 cups iceberg lettuce

Instructions

1. Place the apples, cilantro, lime, cucumber, ginger, and lettuce in your juicer and process them into juice.
2. Pour it into 2 glasses and serve immediately.

HEART DISEASE

- Cucumber contains bioactive compounds such as flavonoids and antioxidants (Naureen et al., 2022). Foods of the Mediterranean diet: citrus, cucumber and grape. They may have protective effects against heart disease. These compounds may help decrease inflammation and blood pressure and improve cholesterol levels. All these factors are important for maintaining heart health.
- Dill contains bioactive compounds that could help improve some risk factors associated with heart disease. For example, dill may improve high blood pressure and high cholesterol levels (Sadeghi et al., 2022). These compounds may also possess antioxidant and anti-inflammatory effects, which may support heart health.
- Bell peppers contain antioxidants and flavonoids, which may help reduce the risk of heart disease. They can decrease inflammation and oxidative stress in your body (Anaya-Esparza et al., 2021). Additionally, bell peppers are low-calorie. They contain many vitamins and minerals, making them a healthy addition to a heart-healthy diet.
- Cantaloupe contains bioactive compounds such as antioxidants and anti-inflammatory agents. These compounds may help reduce the risk of heart disease by improving factors like blood pressure, cholesterol levels, and inflammation (Medeiros et al., 2020).

CUCUMBER DILL JUICE

Prep Time: 10 minutes | **Total Time:** 10 minutes | **Serves:** 2

Nutrition Information (Serving Size: 1 glass of cucumber dill juice)

Calories: 45 kcal	**Carbohydrates:** 9.2g	**Fats:** 0.6g
Protein: 3.6g	**Sugar:** 2.2g	**Fiber:** 3.4g
Sodium: 31mg	**Cholesterol:** 0mg	

Ingredients

- 3 medium English cucumbers
- 1 bunch of dill
- 1 lemon, peeled, quartered

Instructions

1. Place the cucumber, dill, and lemons in your juicer and process them into juice.
2. Pour it into 2 glasses and serve immediately.

SWEET BELL PEPPER JUICE

Prep Time: 10 minutes | **Total Time:** 10 minutes | **Serves:** 2

Nutrition Information (Serving Size: 1 glass of sweet pepper juice)

Calories: 141 kcal	**Carbohydrates:** 34.9g	**Fats:** 0.3g
Protein: 3.1g	**Sugar:** 24.7g	**Fiber:** 7.9g
Sodium: 102mg	**Cholesterol:** 0mg	

Ingredients

- 1/2 medium pineapple, cut into 1-inch chunks
- 2 large red bell peppers
- 2 large oranges
- 2 large carrots

Instructions

1. Place the pineapples, bell peppers, oranges, and carrots in your juicer and process them into juice.
2. Pour it into 2 glasses and serve immediately.

CANTALOUPE JUICE

Prep Time: 10 minutes | **Total Time:** 10 minutes | **Serves:** 2

Nutrition Information (Serving Size: 1 glass of cantaloupe juice)

Calories: 95 kcal **Carbohydrates:** 23.1g **Fats:** 0.2g

Protein: 1.7g **Sugar:** 16.4g **Fiber:** 4.4g

Sodium: 76mg **Cholesterol:** 0mg

Ingredients

- 1 medium cantaloupe
- 1 medium orange, peeled, quartered
- 3 medium carrots, peeled

Instructions

1. Place the cantaloupe, orange, and carrots in your juicer and process them into juice.
2. Pour it into 2 glasses and serve immediately.

INFLUENZA

- Tomatoes contain bioactive compounds like vitamin C and carotenoids, which have antioxidant and anti-inflammatory properties (Kumar et al., 2020). These compounds may help strengthen the immune response and reduce the severity of flu symptoms.
- Watermelon contains bioactive compounds such as vitamins, minerals, and antioxidants, which can aid the immune system (Suleria et al., 2022). These compounds may help alleviate flu symptoms and promote recovery.
- Strawberries contain bioactive compounds such as vitamin C, flavonoids, and antioxidants, which have immune-boosting properties (Newerli-Guz et al., 2023). These compounds may help reduce the severity of flu symptoms and promote recovery.
- Kiwi contains bioactive compounds such as vitamin C, vitamin E, and polyphenols. These compounds have antioxidant and immune-boosting properties (Hunter et al., 2016). They may help decrease the severity of flu symptoms and help you recover faster.
- Kale contains important vitamins, minerals, and antioxidants, such as vitamin C, vitamin K, and flavonoids. These compounds which have immune-boosting properties (Desai, 2021). They may help decrease the severity of flu symptoms and speed up recovery.

TOMATO WATERMELON REFRESHER

Prep Time: 10 minutes | **Total Time:** 10 minutes | **Serves:** 2

Nutrition Information (Serving Size: 1 glass of tomato watermelon refresher)

Calories: 62 kcal   **Carbohydrates:** 16.8g   **Fats:** 0.3g

Protein: 1.7g   **Sugar:** 13.4g   **Fiber:** 2.3g

Sodium: 11mg   **Cholesterol:** 0mg

Ingredients

- ½ medium watermelon, cut into 1-inch pieces
- 2 medium Roma tomatoes
- 1 medium grapefruit, peeled, quartered

Instructions

1. Place the watermelon, tomatoes, and grapefruit in your juicer and process them into juice.
2. Pour it into 2 glasses and serve immediately.

STRAWBERRY KIWI JUICE

Prep Time: 10 minutes | **Total Time:** 10 minutes | **Serves:** 2

Nutrition Information (Serving Size: 1 glass of strawberry kiwi juice)

Calories: 137 kcal   **Carbohydrates:** 32.8g   **Fats:** 1.4g

Protein: 3.4g   **Sugar:** 19.9g   **Fiber:** 7.4g

Sodium: 8mg   **Cholesterol:** 0mg

Ingredients

- 1 cup strawberries, trimmed, halved
- 2 medium kiwis, halved
- 1/2 lemon, peeled
- 1/4 cup mint leaves

Instructions

1. Place the strawberry, kiwis, lemon, and mint in your juicer and process them into juice.
2. Pour it into 2 glasses and serve immediately.

TOMATO KALE CELERY JUICE

Prep Time: 10 minutes | **Total Time:** 10 minutes | **Serves:** 2

Nutrition Information (Serving Size: 1 glass of tomato kale celery juice)

Calories: 91 kcal

Carbohydrates: 11.5g

Fats: 0.8g

Protein: 5.4g

Sugar: 4g

Fiber: 5.3g

Sodium: 102mg

Cholesterol: 0mg

Ingredients

- 2 medium tomatoes, quartered
- 2 medium stalks celery
- 1 bunch kale
- 1 lemon, peeled, quartered

Instructions

1. Place the tomatoes, celery, kale, and lemon in your juicer and process them into juice.
2. Pour it into 2 glasses and serve immediately.

LIVER ISSUES

- Sweet potatoes contain vitamins, minerals, and antioxidants. These nutrients have been linked to liver protection and regeneration (Oki et al., 2017). They may help reduce liver inflammation and oxidative stress and improve liver function.
- Butternut squash is rich in L-citrulline and L-arginine (Mulwa et al., 2020). These compounds act as antioxidants. They may help decrease inflammation and oxidative stress and help detoxify the liver.
- Blueberries contain bioactive compounds such as antioxidants and polyphenols, which have been linked to liver protection and improvement in liver function (Ma et al., 2018).
- Watermelon contains antioxidants, vitamins, and minerals. They can help protect your liver and improve liver functioning (Maoto et al., 2019).
- Sweet orange peel contains flavonoids and antioxidants. These compounds may support liver health by reducing oxidative stress and inflammation. They may also help reduce the risk of liver damage induced by certain substances, such as cyclophosphamide, which may have a toxic effect on the liver.

AUTUMN RAIN

Prep Time: 10 minutes | **Total Time:** 10 minutes | **Serves:** 2

Nutrition Information (Serving Size: 1 glass of autumn rain)

Calories: 156 kcal	**Carbohydrates:** 38.8g	**Fats:** 3g
Protein: 2.4g	**Sugar:** 16.5g	**Fiber:** 6.3g
Sodium: 87mg	**Cholesterol:** 0mg	

Ingredients

- 1 medium sweet potato
- 3 medium carrots
- 1/2 medium butternut squash, peeled, cut into 1-inch pieces
- 1 medium radish
- 1 medium gala apple
- 1/2 medium lemon, peeled
- 1-inch ginger

Instructions

1. Place the sweet potato, carrots, butternut squash, radish, apple, lemon, and ginger in your juicer and process them into juice.
2. Pour it into 2 glasses and serve immediately.

BERRY WATERMELON BLAST

Prep Time: 10 minutes | **Total Time:** 10 minutes | **Serves:** 2

Nutrition Information (Serving Size: 1 glass of berry watermelon blast)

Calories: 171 kcal	**Carbohydrates:** 45g	**Fats:** 0.6g
Protein: 3.1g	**Sugar:** 33.1g	**Fiber:** 8.3g
Sodium: 7mg	**Cholesterol:** 0mg	

Ingredients

- 1 cup strawberries, trimmed, quartered
- 1 cup raspberries
- 1/2 cup blueberries
- 1 medium pomegranate quartered
- 2 cups watermelon, cut into 1-inch pieces
- 1/4 cup mint

Instructions

1. Place the strawberries, raspberries, pomegranate, watermelon, and mint in your juicer and process them into juice.
2. Pour it into 2 glasses and serve immediately.

CITRUS COOLER

Prep Time: 10 minutes | **Total Time:** 10 minutes | **Serves:** 2

Nutrition Information (Serving Size: 1 glass of citrus cooler)

Calories: 181 kcal   **Carbohydrates:** 47.3g   **Fats:** 0.7g

Protein: 2.6g   **Sugar:** 34.3g   **Fiber:** 7.4g

Sodium: 3mg   **Cholesterol:** 0mg

Ingredients

- 2 medium oranges, peeled, quartered
- 2 cups pineapple, cut into 1-inch chunks
- 1 lime, peeled, quartered
- 1 medium grapefruit, peeled, quartered
- 1-inch ginger

Instructions

1. Place the oranges, pineapples, lime, grapefruit, and ginger in your juicer and process them into juice.
2. Pour it into 2 glasses and serve immediately.

PSORIASIS

- Mangos contain vitamin C, beta-carotene, and phenolic acids, which have antioxidant properties. These nutrients can help protect skin cells from oxidative stress, stimulate collagen production, and prevent damage caused by UV radiation (Flores-Balderas et al., 2023). Overall, these properties could help individuals with psoriasis by supporting skin health and reducing inflammation associated with the condition.
- Guavas are high in vitamin B12 and folic acid. They could help you manage psoriasis by providing nutrients that support skin health and immune functioning (Vora et al., 2020).
- Psoriasis is linked to metabolic syndrome and cardiovascular disease. Consuming blueberries may help alleviate this skin condition by addressing underlying metabolic and cardiovascular issues (Ivarsson et al., 2023).
- Grapes contain anthocyanidins and resveratrol. Anthocyanidins help reduce inflammation and oxidative stress in the body, which are key factors for developing psoriasis. Resveratrol also has antioxidant and anti-inflammatory properties (Szpadel et al., 2022). Both compounds may help alleviate symptoms of psoriasis by regulating the immune response and decreasing inflammation in the skin.
- Arugula is rich in antioxidants, which may be beneficial for individuals with psoriasis. They may protect against the harmful effects of free radicals, potentially improving skin lesions associated with psoriasis (Garbicz et al., 2021).

MANGO GUAVA JUICE

Prep Time: 10 minutes | **Total Time:** 10 minutes | **Serves:** 2

Nutrition Information (Serving Size: 1 glass of mango guava juice)

Calories: 181 kcal	**Carbohydrates:** 33.9g	**Fats:** 4.4g
Protein: 3.1g	**Sugar:** 24.8g	**Fiber:** 6.8g
Sodium: 212mg	**Cholesterol:** 0mg	

Ingredients

- 2 large mangoes, cut into 1-inch pieces
- 2 medium guavas, quartered
- 1 large carrot, peeled
- 1-inch fresh ginger

Instructions

1. Place the mangoes, guavas, carrots, and ginger in your juicer and process them into juice.
2. Pour it into 2 glasses and serve immediately.

BLUEBERRY GRAPE JUICE

Prep Time: 10 minutes | **Total Time:** 10 minutes | **Serves:** 2

Nutrition Information (Serving Size: 1 glass of blueberry grape juice)

Calories: 169 kcal	**Carbohydrates:** 40.6g	**Fats:** 0.7g
Protein: 4g	**Sugar:** 28.6g	**Fiber:** 9.2g
Sodium: 13mg	**Cholesterol:** 0mg	

Ingredients

- 1 medium English cucumber
- 1 cup spinach
- 1 1/2 cups blueberries
- 1 cup blackberries
- 1 1/2 cups red grapes

Instructions

1. Place the mangoes, guavas, carrots, and ginger in your juicer and process them into juice.
2. Pour it into 2 glasses and serve immediately.

ARUGULA KALE GREEN JUICE

Prep Time: 10 minutes | **Total Time:** 10 minutes | **Serves:** 2

Nutrition Information (Serving Size: 1 glass of mango guava juice)

Calories: 135 kcal	**Carbohydrates:** 29.6g	**Fats:** 0.3g
Protein: 7.1g	**Sugar:** 12.1g	**Fiber:** 6.5g
Sodium: 133mg	**Cholesterol:** 0mg	

Ingredients

- 4 cups baby arugula
- 1 bunch kale
- 1 grapefruit, peeled, quartered
- 1 Granny Smith apple
- 4 medium celery stalks
- 1-inch ginger

Instructions

1. Place the arugula, kale, grapefruit, apple, celery, and ginger in your juicer and process them into juice.
2. Pour it into 2 glasses and serve immediately.

DIARRHEA

- Papaya can be used to manage digestive issues like diarrhea due to its antimicrobial and anti-inflammatory properties (Amzad et al., 2020).
- Ginger has antimicrobial and anti-inflammatory properties (Claudya et al., 2023). It may help alleviate diarrhea symptoms and promote digestive health.
- Apricots can soften the stool (Tabrizi et al., 2020). They might help alleviate diarrhea by making bowel movements less watery and more formed. Additionally, this could reduce the frequency and urgency of bowel movements associated with diarrhea.
- Sweet potatoes are rich in fiber (Jones & de Brauw, 2015). They may add bulk to stool and improve bowel movements, which may help relieve symptoms of diarrhea.
- Apples contain polyphenols and pectin, which may help regulate bowel movements and alleviate symptoms of diarrhea (Ribeiro et al., 2021).

ANTI-DIARRHEA TONIC

Prep Time: 10 minutes | **Total Time:** 10 minutes | **Serves:** 2

Nutrition Information (Serving Size: 1 glass of anti-diarrhea tonic)

Calories: 75 kcal   **Carbohydrates:** 17.2g   **Fats:** 0.3g

Protein: 2.4g   **Sugar:** 8.2g   **Fiber:** 3.7g

Sodium: 154mg   **Cholesterol:** 0mg

Ingredients

- 2 medium carrots
- 2 medium stalks celery
- 1/2 medium papaya
- 2 cups spinach
- 1/4 cup parsley
- 1-inch piece ginger

Instructions

1. Place the carrots, celery, papaya, spinach, parsley, and ginger in your juicer and process them into juice.
2. Pour it into 2 glasses and serve immediately.

APRICOT SWEET POTATO JUICE

Prep Time: 10 minutes | **Total Time:** 10 minutes | **Serves:** 2

Nutrition Information (Serving Size: 1 glass of apricot sweet potato juice)

Calories: 172 kcal   **Carbohydrates:** 42.6g   **Fats:** 0.5g

Protein: 9g   **Sugar:** 22.6g   **Fiber:** 7.6g

Sodium: 65mg   **Cholesterol:** 0mg

Ingredients

- 2 medium oranges, peeled, quartered.
- 2 medium carrots, peeled
- 1 medium sweet potato
- 1-inch turmeric
- 2 medium apricots

Instructions

1. Place the oranges, carrots, sweet potato, turmeric, and apricots in your juicer and process them into juice.
2. Pour it into 2 glasses and serve immediately.

CRANBERRY APPLE COOLER

Prep Time: 10 minutes | **Total Time:** 10 minutes | **Serves:** 2

Nutrition Information (Serving Size: 1 glass of cranberry apple cooler)

Calories: 117 kcal

Carbohydrates: 26.5g

Fats: 0.4g

Protein: 0.7g

Sugar: 22g

Fiber: 3.6g

Sodium: 0mg

Cholesterol: 0mg

Ingredients

- 2 medium gala apples, cored, quartered
- 1 cup cranberries
- 1 cup red grapes

Instructions

1. Place the apples, cranberries, and grapes in your juicer and process them into juice.
2. Pour it into 2 glasses and serve immediately.

OBESITY

- Oxidative stress may lead to diseases like cancer and obesity. Cucumbers contain compounds like cucurbitacins B and E, which act as antioxidants (Rolnik & Olas, 2020). They help counteract oxidative stress and mitigate the risk of obesity-related health issues.
- Cilantro contains polyphenols, which may improve or reduce the effects of obesity (Scandar et al., 2023). They may aid in weight management or mitigate some health risks associated with obesity.
- Red cabbage can help in managing inflammation in overweight and obese adults. Additionally, some varieties of red cabbage may inhibit enzymes that break down these fats and carbohydrates, helping to manage weight (Garcia-Ibañez et al., 2021).
- Mint can regulate various metabolic processes. It may help reduce body weight, fat accumulation, and related metabolic disorders by influencing your appetite, fat metabolism, and inflammation (Ali-Shtayeh et al., 2019).

CUCUMBER CILANTRO JUICE

Prep Time: 10 minutes | **Total Time:** 10 minutes | **Serves:** 2

Nutrition Information (Serving Size: 1 glass of cucumber cilantro juice)

Calories: 76 kcal	**Carbohydrates:** 19.3g	**Fats:** 0.3g
Protein: 2.6g	**Sugar:** 12.5g	**Fiber:** 4.7g
Sodium: 1mg	**Cholesterol:** 0mg	

Ingredients

- 3 medium English cucumbers
- 1/2 cup cilantro
- 1 lime, peeled, quartered
- 1 medium grapefruit, peeled, quartered
- 1 medium orange, peeled, quartered

Instructions

1. Place the cucumber, lime, grapefruit, and orange in your juicer and process them into juice.
2. Pour it into 2 glasses and serve immediately.

RED CABBAGE JUICE

Prep Time: 10 minutes | **Total Time:** 10 minutes | **Serves:** 2

Nutrition Information (Serving Size: 1 glass of red cabbage juice)

Calories: 98 kcal	**Carbohydrates:** 25.2g	**Fats:** 0.3g
Protein: 2.3g	**Sugar:** 13.7g	**Fiber:** 6.7g
Sodium: 32mg	**Cholesterol:** 0mg	

Ingredients

- 1/4 of a medium head of red cabbage
- 1 bunch green onions
- 1 medium gala apple
- 1 medium English cucumber
- 1 lime, peeled, quartered
- 1 1/2-inch piece of fresh ginger

Instructions

1. Place the cabbage, green onions, apple, cucumber, lime, and ginger in your juicer and process them into juice.
2. Pour it into 2 glasses and serve immediately.

MINT PARSLEY REFRESHER

Prep Time: 10 minutes | **Total Time:** 10 minutes | **Serves:** 2

Nutrition Information (Serving Size: 1 glass of parsley mint refresher)

Calories: 76 kcal

Carbohydrates: 17.3g

Fats: 0.6g

Protein: 2.6g

Sugar: 9.1g

Fiber: 6.8g

Sodium: 25mg

Cholesterol: 0mg

Ingredients

- 1 bunch flat-leaf parsley
- 1 bunch mint
- 1 medium gala apple, cored, quartered
- 1 medium English cucumber
- 1 lemon, peeled, cored

Instructions

1. Place the parsley, mint, apple, cucumber, and lemon in your juicer and process them into juice.
2. Pour it into 2 glasses and serve immediately.

BLADDER ISSUES

- Blueberries contain bioactive compounds with anti-inflammatory and antioxidant properties. They may help decrease the risk of urinary tract infections and other bladder-related issues. These compounds may also support overall urinary tract health by decreasing inflammation and oxidative stress in the bladder (Miyazaki et al., 2020).
- Cranberry juice has compounds called proanthocyanidins that stop bacteria from sticking to the bladder walls. These compounds help prevent bacteria from causing infections and get rid of them when you pee (Sujana et al., 2016).
- Pomegranates contain punicalagin and ellagic acid. These compounds may have protective effects against bladder cancer by discouraging the growth of cancer cells and facilitating their destruction (Wigner et al., 2022).
- Celery contains compounds like apigenin and luteolin. They possess anti-inflammatory and antioxidant properties, which could reduce inflammation and oxidative stress in the bladder (Sarshar et al., 2018).

BERRY POWER

Prep Time: 10 minutes | **Total Time:** 10 minutes | **Serves:** 2

Nutrition Information (Serving Size: 1 glass of berry power)

Calories: 97 kcal

Carbohydrates: 16.8g

Fats: 0.6g

Protein: 0.8g

Sugar: 8.9g

Fiber: 3.7g

Sodium: 1mg

Cholesterol: 0mg

Ingredients

- 1 cup raspberries
- 1 cup cranberries
- 1 cup blueberries
- 1 lime, peeled, quartered

Instructions

1. Place the raspberries, cranberries, blueberries, and lime in your juicer and process them into juice.
2. Pour it into 2 glasses and serve immediately.

POMEGRANATE CELERY JUICE

Prep Time: 10 minutes | **Total Time:** 10 minutes | **Serves:** 2

Nutrition Information (Serving Size: 1 glass of pomegranate celery juice)

Calories: 125 kcal

Carbohydrates: 31.2g

Fats: 0.3g

Protein: 2.3g

Sugar: 22.7g

Fiber: 3.1g

Sodium: 60mg

Cholesterol: 0mg

Ingredients

- 2 medium pomegranates
- 3 medium stalks of celery
- 1 cup watercress
- 1-inch ginger

Instructions

1. Place the pomegranate, celery, watercress, and ginger in your juicer and process them into juice.
2. Pour it into 2 glasses and serve immediately.

ULCERS

- Cabbage juice could help heal ulcers. It is rich in glutamine, which may have protective effects on the stomach lining (Shoaib et al., 2016).
- Cucumber has antioxidant and anti-inflammatory properties that may help in the treatment or management of ulcers (Sahu & Sahu, 2015).
- Radishes may help health peptic ulcers. Radishes contain compounds that possess antioxidant and cytoprotective properties (Luo et al., 2018). These compounds help protect the stomach lining from damage caused by excess stomach acid and bacterial infections, which can lead to peptic ulcers.
- Raspberries may help protect the stomach lining and promote ulcer healing. They may combat oxidative stress and inflammation, which may cause ulcers to develop (Nesello et al., 2017).
- Kale contains glucoraphanin, which can be converted into sulforaphane. Sulforaphane can inhibit the bacteria Helicobacter pylori which can cause ulcers and stomach cancer (Shafi et al., 2022). Therefore, kale can be used to treat gastric and peptic ulcers.

ULCER RELIEF

Prep Time: 10 minutes | **Total Time:** 10 minutes | **Serves:** 2

Nutrition Information (Serving Size: 1 glass of ulcer relief)

Calories: 125 kcal   **Carbohydrates:** 36.5g   **Fats:** 0.1g

Protein: 4.7g   **Sugar:** 18g   **Fiber:** 9.8g

Sodium: 230mg   **Cholesterol:** 0mg

Ingredients

- 1/2 medium head of green cabbage
- 4 medium stalks of celery
- 4 medium carrots
- 1 medium Granny Smith apple
- 2 large red bell peppers, seeded, roughly chopped.

Instructions

1. Place the cabbage, celery, carrots, apple, and bell pepper in your juicer and process them into juice.
2. Pour it into 2 glasses and serve immediately.

ULCER AID

Prep Time: 10 minutes | **Total Time:** 10 minutes | **Serves:** 2

Nutrition Information (Serving Size: 1 glass of ulcer aid)

Calories: 96 kcal   **Carbohydrates:** 21.6g   **Fats:** 0.5g

Protein: 6.8g   **Sugar:** 9.8g   **Fiber:** 6.6g

Sodium: 73mg   **Cholesterol:** 0mg

Ingredients

- 1/2 medium head of red cabbage, roughly chopped
- 2 medium English cucumbers
- 2 cups of alfalfa sprouts
- 1 medium radish, halved
- 1 cup broccoli florets

Instructions

1. Place the cabbage, cucumbers, alfalfa sprouts, radish, and broccoli in your juicer and process them into juice.
2. Pour it into 2 glasses and serve immediately.

TUMMY SOOTHER

Prep Time: 10 minutes | **Total Time:** 10 minutes | **Serves:** 2

Nutrition Information (Serving Size: 1 glass of tummy soother)

Calories: 157 kcal	**Carbohydrates:** 35.9g	**Fats:** 0.7g
Protein: 5.7g	**Sugar:** 13.5g	**Fiber:** 11.2g
Sodium: 190mg	**Cholesterol:** 0mg	

Ingredients

- 5 medium carrots, peeled
- 1/4 medium head of red cabbage
- 3 medium celery stalks
- 1 cup raspberries
- 1 bunch kale

Instructions

1. Place the carrots, cabbage, celery, raspberries, and kale in your juicer and process them into juice.
2. Pour it into 2 glasses and serve immediately.

ANEMIA

- Beet juice may help you manage anemia. They contain compounds that can boost iron levels in the blood, which can improve symptoms of anemia (Babarykin et al., 2019). Additionally, beet juice has anti-inflammatory, antioxidant, and anticancer properties, which could contribute to overall health.
- Carrots contain high levels of iron, folic acid, vitamin C, and protein (Mohamed Ali et al., 2016). These nutrients are important for supporting healthy blood production and may help alleviate symptoms of anemia.
- Spinach is rich in iron. It is a crucial nutrient for red blood cell production, making it beneficial for individuals with anemia (Santoyo-Sánchez et al., 2015). Additionally, spinach contains other essential vitamins and minerals like folic acid that support overall health and may help alleviate symptoms of anemia.
- Kiwi fruit can help increase iron absorption in the body, leading to higher hemoglobin levels and potentially reducing the risk or severity of anemia (Dwivedi et al., 2020).

IRON JUICE

Prep Time: 10 minutes | **Total Time:** 10 minutes | **Serves:** 2

Nutrition Information (Serving Size: 1 glass of iron juice)

Calories: 138 kcal   **Carbohydrates:** 32.6g   **Fats:** 0.6g

Protein: 2.4g   **Sugar:** 23.4g   **Fiber:** 6.5g

Sodium: 133mg   **Cholesterol:** 0mg

Ingredients

- 1 medium beet, peeled, quartered
- 2 medium carrots, peeled
- 2 medium gala apples, cored, quartered
- 1-inch piece of ginger
- ½ lemon, peeled
- 1 medium red bell pepper, seeded, roughly chopped
- 1 cup Swiss chard, roughly chopped

Instructions

1. Place the beet, carrots, apples, ginger, lemon, bell pepper, and Swiss chard in your juicer and process them into juice.
2. Pour it into 2 glasses and serve immediately.

IRON VEGETABLE

Prep Time: 10 minutes | **Total Time:** 10 minutes | **Serves:** 2

Nutrition Information (Serving Size: 1 glass of iron vegetable)

Calories: 72 kcal   **Carbohydrates:** 15.2g   **Fats:** 0.2g

Protein: 4.3g   **Sugar:** 3.4g   **Fiber:** 4g

Sodium: 138mg   **Cholesterol:** 0mg

Ingredients

- 2 cups raw baby spinach
- 1 medium tomato
- 2 cups beet greens
- 2 medium carrots
- 1/2 medium cucumber
- 1 Swiss chard leaf
- 3 kale leaves
- 1/4 cup parsley

Instructions

1. Place the spinach, tomato, beet greens, carrots, cucumber, Swiss chard, kale, and parsley in your juicer and process them into juice.
2. Pour it into 2 glasses and serve immediately.

GREEN FIGHTER

Prep Time: 10 minutes | **Total Time:** 10 minutes | **Serves:** 2

Nutrition Information (Serving Size: 1 glass of green fighter)

Calories: 176 kcal
Carbohydrates: 38.5g
Fats: 1.5g

Protein: 6.7g
Sugar: 24g
Fiber: 8.6g

Sodium: 135mg
Cholesterol: 0mg

Ingredients

- 2 medium kiwi
- 1 cup green grapes
- 4 cups baby spinach
- 1 lemon, peeled, quartered

Instructions

1. Place the kiwi, grapes, spinach, and lemon in your juicer and process them into juice.
2. Pour it into 2 glasses and serve immediately.

BRAIN DISEASES

- Beets contain high levels of nitrate. Nitrate may have a protective effect against stroke by enhancing blood flow and decreasing blood pressure, particularly in hypertensive individuals (Khatri et al., 2016).
- Pomegranates contain antioxidants and anti-inflammatory compounds that may help decrease the risk of stroke. They may also improve outcomes after stroke by protecting brain cells from damage and stimulating recovery (Bellone et al., 2018).
- Oxidative stress may play a role in the progression of encephalitis. Bell peppers are rich in antioxidants. They may help protect against oxidative damage in the brain (Łuczaj et al., 2015). This could help you manage encephalitis.
- Cucumbers contain cucurbitacin B. This compound may have properties that could help alleviate certain aspects of MS by modulating immune responses and inflammation (Reiszadeh-Jahromi et al., 2022).
- Red onions contain quercetin. This compound has anti-inflammatory and antioxidant properties (Javanbakht et al., 2023). It may fight swelling and help protect cells from damage. This could maybe help calm down the body's overactive defenses and ease swelling in multiple sclerosis.

STROKE RECOVERY

Prep Time: 10 minutes | **Total Time:** 10 minutes | **Serves:** 2

Nutrition Information (Serving Size: 1 glass of stroke recovery)

Calories: 148 kcal   **Carbohydrates:** 35.6g   **Fats:** 0.4g

Protein: 2.7g   **Sugar:** 27.8g   **Fiber:** 4.5g

Sodium: 102mg   **Cholesterol:** 0mg

Ingredients

- 2 medium beets
- 1 large carrot, peeled
- 1 medium gala apple
- 1 medium pomegranate
- 1-inch ginger

Instructions

1. Place the beets, carrot, apple, pomegranate, and ginger in your juicer and process them into juice.
2. Pour it into 2 glasses and serve immediately.

ENCEPHALITIS RELIEF

Prep Time: 10 minutes | **Total Time:** 10 minutes | **Serves:** 2

Nutrition Information (Serving Size: 1 glass of encephalitis relief)

Calories: 206 kcal   **Carbohydrates:** 49g   **Fats:** 0.4g

Protein: 7g   **Sugar:** 29.1g   **Fiber:** 15.4g

Sodium: 178mg   **Cholesterol:** 0mg

Ingredients

- 2 medium cucumbers
- 1 medium yellow squash
- 6 stalks celery
- 2 medium gala apples
- 1 medium bulb fennel, roughly chopped
- 1 medium yellow bell pepper, seeded, roughly chopped

Instructions

1. Place the cucumbers, squash, celery, apples, fennel, and bell pepper in your juicer and process them into juice.
2. Pour it into 2 glasses and serve immediately.

MS BOOSTER

Prep Time: 10 minutes | **Total Time:** 10 minutes | **Serves:** 2

Nutrition Information (Serving Size: 1 glass of MS booster)

Calories: 170 kcal	**Carbohydrates:** 37.9g	**Fats:** 0g
Protein: 9.2g	**Sugar:** 14.7g	**Fiber:** 7.2g
Sodium: 110mg	**Cholesterol:** 0mg	

Ingredients

- 2 medium cucumbers
- 2 medium stalks of celery
- 4 bunches of kale
- 1/2 medium red onion
- 1 cup black grapes
- 1/2 lemon, peeled

Instructions

1. Place the cucumbers, celery, kale, red onion, black grapes, and lemon in your juicer and process them into juice.
2. Pour it into 2 glasses and serve immediately.

THYROID

- Mercury can cause harmful effects on genes, immune reactions, and cells' ability to protect themselves from damage (Pamphlett et al., 2021). It may increase the risks of thyroid cancers, autoimmune thyroiditis, and hypothyroidism. Plums are rich in pectin. Pectin may remove heavy metals like mercury from the body (Zhexenbay et al., 2020).
- Brassica vegetables like cauliflower and arugula contain antioxidants and vitamins that help protect the body from diseases. They also have compounds called isothiocyanates that help our body get rid of harmful substances. They can activate certain enzymes that help detoxify our body and reduce oxidative stress (Saban, n.d.).
- Cilantro contains metal-binding proteins that could help the body eliminate mercury and reduce the absorption of lead (Danailova et al., 2022). This could prevent the harmful effects of heavy metal toxicity, which may contribute to thyroid dysfunction.

PLUM MAGIC

Prep Time: 10 minutes | **Total Time:** 10 minutes | **Serves:** 2

Nutrition Information (Serving Size: 1 glass of plum magic)

Calories: 173 kcal

Protein: 3.4g

Sodium: 1mg

Carbohydrates: 44.4g

Sugar: 23.4g

Cholesterol: 0mg

Fats: 1.7g

Fiber: 6.1g

Ingredients

- 6 ripe plums, chopped with the pit removed
- 1 medium pear
- 1/2 lime, peeled

Instructions

1. Place the plums, pear, and lime in your juicer and process them into juice.
2. Pour it into 2 glasses and serve immediately.

THYROID SOOTHER

Prep Time: 10 minutes | **Total Time:** 10 minutes | **Serves:** 2

Nutrition Information (Serving Size: 1 glass of thyroid soother)

Calories: 114 kcal

Protein: 2.9g

Sodium: 103mg

Carbohydrates: 27.4g

Sugar: 15.5g

Cholesterol: 0mg

Fats: 0.5g

Fiber: 6.6g

Ingredients

- 1 medium gala apple, cored, quartered
- 1 cup arugula
- 1/2 cup cilantro
- 1/2 cup parsley
- 4 medium carrots, peeled
- ½ lime, peeled
- 1-inch piece of ginger

Instructions

1. Place the apple, arugula, cilantro, parsley, black, carrots, lime, and ginger in your juicer and process them into juice.
2. Pour it into 2 glasses and serve immediately

CILANTRO CAULIFLOWER REMEDY

Prep Time: 10 minutes | **Total Time:** 10 minutes | **Serves:** 2

Nutrition Information (Serving Size: 1 glass of cilantro cauliflower remedy)

Calories: 122 kcal

Carbohydrates: 29.4g

Fats: 0.4g

Protein: 4.8g

Sugar: 14.4g

Fiber: 7.8g

Sodium: 160mg

Cholesterol: 0mg

Ingredients

- 5 medium stalks of celery
- 2 medium Granny Smith apples, sliced
- 1 bunch of cilantro
- 2-inches ginger
- 1/2 medium head cauliflower, roughly chopped

Instructions

1. Place the celery, apples, cilantro, ginger, and cauliflower in your juicer and process them into juice.
2. Pour it into 2 glasses and serve immediately.

JOINT PAIN

- Pineapples contain bromelain. Bromelain is an enzyme that contains anti-inflammatory properties. It may help decrease inflammation and alleviate joint pain (Varilla et al., 2021).
- Leafy greens like spinach and kale are rich in nutrients like vitamins, minerals, and antioxidants, which may help decrease inflammation and relieve joint pain (Wallace et al., 2019).
- Blackberries contain anthocyanins, which could be good for your joints. Research has shown that eating fruits with these compounds might help reduce inflammation and manage conditions like arthritis and obesity (Pomilio et al., 2022).
- Cranberries contain compounds that may help reduce inflammation and oxidative stress in the joints, thereby alleviating pain and discomfort from conditions like arthritis (Kelley et al., 2018). Additionally, cranberries possess antioxidant properties that could contribute to overall joint health.
- Grapes contain compounds like polyphenols and antioxidants that have anti-inflammatory properties (Masud Parvez & Akanda, 2019). These compounds may decrease inflammation in your joints.

JOINT RELIEF

Prep Time: 10 minutes | **Total Time:** 10 minutes | **Serves:** 2

Nutrition Information (Serving Size: 1 glass of joint relief)

Calories: 202 kcal	**Carbohydrates:** 44.3g	**Fats:** 1.3g
Protein: 6.1g	**Sugar:** 28.6g	**Fiber:** 10.1g
Sodium: 105mg	**Cholesterol:** 0mg	

Ingredients

- 2 cups pineapple, cut into 1-inch chunks
- 1 medium pear
- 2 cups spinach
- 1 bunch kale
- 1 bunch parsley
- 1 medium carrot, peeled
- 1 medium grapefruit

Instructions

1. Place the pineapple, pear, spinach, kale, parsley, carrot, and grapefruit in your juicer and process them into juice.
2. Pour it into 2 glasses and serve immediately.

JOINT AID

Prep Time: 10 minutes | **Total Time:** 10 minutes | **Serves:** 2

Nutrition Information (Serving Size: 1 glass of joint aid)

Calories: 194 kcal	**Carbohydrates:** 47.6g	**Fats:** 1.1g
Protein: 4.1g	**Sugar:** 32.8g	**Fiber:** 14.8g
Sodium: 10mg	**Cholesterol:** 0mg	

Ingredients

- 2 cups blackberries
- 1/2 medium cucumber
- 2 medium golden delicious apples
- 1/2 medium lemon
- 1-inch turmeric
- 1/2 medium cantaloupe, peeled, cut into 1-inch pieces

Instructions

1. Place the blackberries, cucumber, apples, lemon, turmeric, and cantaloupe in your juicer and process them into juice.
2. Pour it into 2 glasses and serve immediately.

RED SOOTHER

Prep Time: 10 minutes | **Total Time:** 10 minutes | **Serves:** 2

Nutrition Information (Serving Size: 1 glass of red soother)

Calories: 124 kcal   **Carbohydrates:** 24.2g   **Fats:** 0.6g

Protein: 3.4g   **Sugar:** 16.4g   **Fiber:** 4.7g

Sodium: 68mg   **Cholesterol:** 0mg

Ingredients

- 1 cup cherries
- 1 cup red grapes
- 1 medium red bell pepper, seeded, roughly chopped.

- 1 bunch kale
- 1 large carrot
- 1-inch ginger
- 1-inch turmeric

Instructions

1. Place the cherries, grapes, bell pepper, kale, carrot, ginger, and turmeric in your juicer and process them into juice.
2. Pour it into 2 glasses and serve immediately.

ARTHRITIS

- Watermelon, nutrients, and phytochemicals may benefit arthritis (Maoto et al., 2019). These compounds act like antioxidants, reducing inflammation, which is a key factor in arthritis.
- Red beets contain pigments called betalains and nitrates. These compounds possess properties that can be beneficial in inflammatory conditions like arthritis. They may reduce oxidative stress, which is known to contribute to inflammation (Dey et al., 2020).
- Strawberries have compounds like polyphenols that may reduce inflammation in the joints. They can also provide relief from arthritis symptoms (Schell et al., 2017).
- Ginger has anti-inflammatory and antioxidant effects. Ginger can help reduce inflammation and pain from arthritis. Additionally, ginger may improve joint function and overall quality of life for arthritis patients (Aryaeian et al., 2019).
- Carrots contain compounds like beta-carotene and polyacetylenes. These compounds may reduce inflammation and oxidative stress in the body. They may help alleviate symptoms of arthritis.
- Turmeric contains a compound called curcumin, which has anti-inflammatory and antioxidant properties. Research shows curcumin may help reduce joint pain and stiffness associated with arthritis. Additionally, turmeric has been suggested to have a protective effect on joint tissues and may help slow the progression of arthritis (Daily et al., 2016).

WATERMELON BEET JUICE

Prep Time: 10 minutes | **Total Time:** 10 minutes | **Serves:** 2

Nutrition Information (Serving Size: 1 glass of watermelon beet juice)

Calories: 195 kcal	**Carbohydrates:** 58.7g	**Fats:** 0.3g
Protein: 3.4g	**Sugar:** 37.5g	**Fiber:** 8.7g
Sodium: 55mg	**Cholesterol:** 0mg	

Ingredients

- 3 cups watermelon, cut into 1-inch pieces
- 1 medium Granny Smith apple, quartered
- 1 medium beet, quartered
- 1 lime, peeled, quartered
- 1/2 cup mint
- 1 serrano pepper, seeded, roughly chopped

Instructions

1. Place the watermelon, apples, beet, lime, mint, and serrano pepper in your juicer and process them into juice.
2. Pour it into 2 glasses and serve immediately.

STRAWBERRY LEMON SHOT

Prep Time: 10 minutes | **Total Time:** 10 minutes | **Serves:** 2

Nutrition Information (Serving Size: 1 glass of strawberry lemon shot)

Calories: 108 kcal	**Carbohydrates:** 27.5g	**Fats:** 1.1g
Protein: 2.7g	**Sugar:** 13.6g	**Fiber:** 7.2g
Sodium: 5mg	**Cholesterol:** 0mg	

Ingredients

- 3 lemons, peeled, quartered
- 3-inches ginger
- 3 cups strawberries, trimmed, halved

Instructions

1. Place the lemons, ginger, and strawberries in your juicer and process them into juice.
2. Pour it into 2 glasses and serve immediately.

SWEET CARROT JUICE

Prep Time: 10 minutes | **Total Time:** 10 minutes | **Serves:** 2

Nutrition Information (Serving Size: 1 glass of sweet carrot juice)

Calories: 202 kcal	**Carbohydrates:** 49.9g	**Fats:** 0.2g
Protein: 4.2g	**Sugar:** 25.8g	**Fiber:** 10.1g
Sodium: 147mg	**Cholesterol:** 0mg	

Ingredients

- 2 medium red bell peppers, seeded, roughly chopped
- 1 medium sweet potato, roughly chopped
- 4 medium carrots, peeled
- 2 medium oranges, peeled, quartered
- 1-inch turmeric

Instructions

1. Place the bell peppers, sweet potato, carrots, oranges, and turmeric in your juicer and process them into juice.
2. Pour it into 2 glasses and serve immediately.

REFERENCES

Abdullah Al Ali. (2023). Overview of the vital roles of macro minerals in the human body. *Journal of Trace Elements and Minerals, 4*, 100076–100076.
https://doi.org/10.1016/j.jtemin.2023.100076

Akhtar, P., Ahmad, I., Jameela, A., Ashfaque, M., & Dr. Begum, Z. (2020). Energizing Effectiveness of Cucumber (Khayarain) For Health. A Review Article. *JETIR November 2020, Volume 7, Issue 11.*
https://odontoanamaria.com/artigos/pepino4.pdf

Al –Taai, E., M. (2016). Protective Effects Of Sweet Orange Peel (Citrus Sinesus L.) The Induction Of Micronuclei Induced By Cyclophosphamide In Human Peripheral Lymphocytes. *Journal of Food Technology Research, 3(1): 28-35.*
https://www.researchgate.net/profile/Ekhlas-
Farhan/publication/303554580_Protective_Effects_of_Sweet_Orange_Peel_Citrus_Sinensis_L
_The_Induction_of_Micronuclei_Induced_by_Cyclophosphamide_in_Human_Peripheral_Lymp
hocytes/links/5c9fcda9299bf11169521167/Protective-Effects-of-Sweet-Orange-Peel-Citrus-
Sinensis-L-The-Induction-of-Micronuclei-Induced-by-Cyclophosphamide-in-Human-Peripheral-
Lymphocytes.pdf

Ali-Shtayeh, M. S., Jamous, R. M., Abu-Zaitoun, S. Y., Khasati, A. I., & Kalbouneh, S. R. (2019). Biological Properties and Bioactive Components ofMentha spicataL. Essential Oil: Focus on Potential Benefits in the Treatment of Obesity, Alzheimer's Disease, Dermatophytosis, and Drug-Resistant Infections. *Evidence-Based Complementary and Alternative Medicine, 2019*, 1–11.
https://doi.org/10.1155/2019/3834265

Amzad Hossain, M., Hitam, S., & Hadidja Ibrahim Ahmed, S. (2020). Pharmacological and toxicological activities of the extracts of papaya leaves used traditionally for the treatment of diarrhea. *Journal of King Saud University - Science, 32*(1), 962-969.
https://doi.org/10.1016/j.jksus.2019.07.006

Anaya-Esparza, L. M., Mora, Z. V. la, Vázquez-Paulino, O., Ascencio, F., & Villarruel-López, A. (2021). Bell Peppers (Capsicum annum L.) Losses and Wastes: Source for Food and Pharmaceutical Applications. *Molecules, 26*(17), 5341.
https://doi.org/10.3390/molecules26175341

Aryaeian, N., Mahmoudi, M., Shahram, F., Poursani, S., Jamshidi, F., & Tavakoli, H. (2019). The effect of ginger supplementation on IL2, TNFα, and IL1β cytokines gene expression levels in

patients with active rheumatoid arthritis: A randomized controlled trial. *Medical Journal of the Islamic Republic of Iran, 33*, 154.
https://doi.org/10.34171/mjiri.33.154

Bahadoran, Z., Mirmiran, P., Kabir, A., Azizi, F., & Ghasemi, A. (2017). The Nitrate-Independent Blood Pressure–Lowering Effect of Beetroot Juice: A Systematic Review and Meta-Analysis. *Advances in Nutrition, 8*(6), 830–838.
https://doi.org/10.3945/an.117.016717

Babarykin, D., Smirnova, G., Pundinsh, I., Vasiljeva, S., Krumina, G., & Agejchenko, V. (2019). Red Beet (Beta vulgaris) Impact on Human Health. *Journal of Biosciences and Medicines, 7*(3), 61–79.
https://doi.org/10.4236/jbm.2019.73007

Bellone, J. A., Murray, J. R., Jorge, P., Fogel, T. G., Kim, M., Wallace, D. R., & Hartman, R. E. (2018). Pomegranate supplementation improves cognitive and functional recovery following ischemic stroke: A randomized trial. *Nutritional Neuroscience, 22*(10), 738–743.
https://doi.org/10.1080/1028415x.2018.1436413

Bhadra P., Banerjee P., & Deb A. (2021). Role of Ginger and its Components in Prevention and Treatment of Common Cold. An Anthology of Nutraceuticals. *New Delhi Publishers,* Article pp.211-226., *ISBN: 978-93-91012-95-3.*
DOI: 10.30954/anthnutraceuticals.17

Bijan Helli, Foroogh Anjirizadeh, Asieh Mehramiri, Davood Shalilahmadi, & Seyed Mahmoud Latifi. (2022). *The Effect of Ginger (Zingiber officinale Rosc.) Consumption in Headache Prophylaxis in Patients with Migraine: A Randomized Placebo-Controlled Clinical Trial. In Press*(In Press).
https://doi.org/10.5812/jjnpp-120449

Binia, A., Jaeger, J., Hu, Y., Singh, A., & Zimmermann, D. (2015). Daily potassium intake and sodium-to-potassium ratio in the reduction of blood pressure: a meta-analysis of randomized controlled trials. *Journal of Hypertension, 33*(8), 1509–1520.
https://doi.org/10.1097/HJH.0000000000000611

Calvano, A., Izuora, K., Oh, E. C., Ebersole, J. L., Lyons, T. J., & Basu, A. (2019). Dietary berries, insulin resistance and type 2 diabetes: an overview of human feeding trials. *Food & Function, 10*(10), 6227–6243.
https://doi.org/10.1039/c9fo01426h

Chen, C.-H., Hsia, C.-C., Hu, P.-A., Yeh, C.-H., Chen, C.-T., Peng, C.-L., Wang, C.-H., & Lee, T.-S. (2023). Bromelain Ameliorates Atherosclerosis by Activating the TFEB-Mediated Autophagy and Antioxidant Pathways. *Antioxidants, 12*(1), 72.
https://doi.org/10.3390/antiox12010072

Chen, L., Zhu, Y., Hu, Z., Wu, S., & Jin, C. (2021). Beetroot as a functional food with huge health benefits: Antioxidant, antitumor, physical function, and chronic metabolomics activity. *Food Science & Nutrition, 9*(11), 6406–6420.
https://doi.org/10.1002/fsn3.2577

Claudya, R., P., Sugiaman, H., S., Labiba, S., I., Utari, M., P., & Gunawan, D. (2023). The therapeutic effects of ginger extract on gastrointestinal disorders to adults. *Science Midwifery*, *11*(1), 251–261.
https://doi.org/10.35335/midwifery.v11i1.1183

Collins, M. W., Saag, K. G., & Singh, J. A. (2019). Is there a role for cherries in the management of gout? *Therapeutic Advances in Musculoskeletal Disease*, *11*.
https://doi.org/10.1177/1759720X19847018

Daily, J. W., Yang, M., & Park, S. (2016). Efficacy of Turmeric Extracts and Curcumin for Alleviating the Symptoms of Joint Arthritis: A Systematic Review and Meta-Analysis of Randomized Clinical Trials. *Journal of Medicinal Food*, *19*(8), 717–729.
https://doi.org/10.1089/jmf.2016.3705

Danailova, Y., Velikova, T., Nikolaev, G., Mitova, Z., Shinkov, A., Gagov, H., & Konakchieva, R. (2022). Nutritional Management of Thyroiditis of Hashimoto. *ProQuest*, *23*(9), 5144.
https://doi.org/10.3390/ijms23095144

Daswani, P. G., Gholkar, M. S., & Birdi, T. J. (2017). Psidium guajava: A Single Plant for Multiple Health Problems of Rural Indian Population. *Pharmacognosy Reviews*, *11*(22), 167–174.
https://doi.org/10.4103/phrev.phrev_17_17

Deding, U., Baatrup, G., Kaalby, L., & Kobaek-Larsen, M. (2023). Carrot Intake and Risk of Developing Cancer: A Prospective Cohort Study. *Nutrients*, *15*(3), 678.
https://doi.org/10.3390/nu15030678

Desai, T. (2021). Increase immunity and fight against corona virus. ~ 108 ~ *International Journal of Home Science*, *7*(3), 108–111.
https://www.homesciencejournal.com/archives/2021/vol7issue3/PartB/7-2-61-589.pdf

Dey, M., Cutolo, M., & Nikiphorou, E. (2020). Beverages in Rheumatoid Arthritis: What to Prefer or to Avoid. *Nutrients*, *12*(10), 3155.
https://doi.org/10.3390/nu12103155

de Oliveira, S. P. A., do Nascimento, H. M. A., Sampaio, K. B., & de Souza, E. L. (2020). A review on bioactive compounds of beet (Beta vulgaris L. subsp. vulgaris) with special emphasis on their beneficial effects on gut microbiota and gastrointestinal health. *Critical Reviews in Food Science and Nutrition*, *61*(12), 2022–2033.
https://doi.org/10.1080/10408398.2020.1768510

Dwivedi, S., Mishra, A., K., Priya, S., Sibtain, F., & Dhami, A. (2020). Potential Health Benefits of Kiwifruits: The King of Fruits. *Issue 4, Volume 5*, 126–131.
https://doi.org/10.46243/jst.2021.v6.i1.pp126-131

Eissa, H. A., Gabrial, S. G. N., S, N. A., Ramadan, M. T., Mohamed, S. S., & Ibrahim, W. A. (2021). Egyptian Batata (Sweet Potato: Ipomoea batatas Lam.) Juice as a Functional Food to Relieve Acid Reflux and Dyspepsia. *Annals of the Romanian Society for Cell Biology*, 4418–4429.
https://annalsofrscb.ro/index.php/journal/article/view/1463

Ezzat-Zadeh, Z., Henning, S. M., Yang, J., Woo, S. L., Lee, R.-P., Huang, J., Thames, G., Gilbuena, I., Tseng, C.-H., Heber, D., & Li, Z. (2021). California strawberry consumption increased the abundance of gut microorganisms related to lean body weight, health and longevity in healthy subjects. *Nutrition Research (New York, N.Y.)*, *85*, 60–70. https://doi.org/10.1016/j.nutres.2020.12.006

Fabjanowicz, M., Różańska, A., Abd Iwahab, N. S., Pereira-Coelho, M., Haas, I. C. da S., Madureira, L. A. dos S., & Płotka-Wasylka, J. (2024). An analytical pproach to determine the health benefits and health risks of consuming berry juices. *Food Chemistry*, *432*, 137219. https://doi.org/10.1016/j.foodchem.2023.137219

Flores-Balderas, X., Peña-Peña, M., Rada, K. M., Alvarez-Alvarez, Y. Q., Guzmán-Martín, C. A., Sánchez-Gloria, J. L., Huang, F., Ruiz-Ojeda, D., Morán-Ramos, S., Springall, R., & Sánchez-Muñoz, F. (2023). Beneficial Effects of Plant-Based Diets on Skin Health and Inflammatory Skin Diseases. *Nutrients*, *15*(13), 2842. https://doi.org/10.3390/nu15132842

Flores-Estrada, J., Cano-Martínez, A., Vargas-González, Á., Castrejón-Téllez, V., Cornejo-Garrido, J., Martínez-Rosas, M., Guarner-Lans, V., & Rubio-Ruíz, M. E. (2023). Hepatoprotective Mechanisms Induced by Spinach Methanolic Extract in Rats with Hyperglycemia—An Immunohistochemical Analysis. *Antioxidants*, *12*(11), 2013. https://doi.org/10.3390/antiox12112013

Garbicz, J., Całyniuk, B., Górski, M., Buczkowska, M., Piecuch, M., Kulik, A., & Rozentryt, P. (2021). Nutritional Therapy in Persons Suffering from Psoriasis. *Nutrients*, *14*(1), 119. https://doi.org/10.3390/nu14010119

Garcia-Ibañez, P., Roses, C., Agudelo, A., Milagro, F. I., Barceló, A. M., Viadel, B., Nieto, J. A., Moreno, D. A., & Carvajal, M. (2021). The Influence of Red Cabbage Extract Nanoencapsulated with Brassica Plasma Membrane Vesicles on the Gut Microbiome of Obese Volunteers. *Foods*, *10*(5), 1038. https://doi.org/10.3390/foods10051038

Green leafy vegetable and lutein intake and multiple health outcomes. (2021). *Food Chemistry*, *360*, 130145. https://doi.org/10.1016/j.foodchem.2021.130145

Gröber, U., Schmidt, J., & Kisters, K. (2015). Magnesium in Prevention and Therapy. *Nutrients*, *7*(9), 8199–8226. https://doi.org/10.3390/nu7095388

Hafez, R. M., Abdel-Rahman, T. M., & Naguib, R. M. (2017). Uric acid in plants and microorganisms: Biological applications and genetics - A review. *Journal of Advanced Research*, *8*(5), 475–486. https://doi.org/10.1016/j.jare.2017.05.003

Henning, S. M., Yang, J., Shao, P., Lee, R.-P., Huang, J., Ly, A., Hsu, M., Lu, Q.-Y., Thames, G., Heber, D., & Li, Z. (2017). Health benefit of vegetable/fruit juice-based diet: Role of microbiome. *Scientific Reports*, *7*(1). https://doi.org/10.1038/s41598-017-02200-6

Herdiana, Y. (2023). Functional Food in Relation to Gastroesophageal Reflux Disease (GERD). *Nutrients*, *15*(16), 3583. https://doi.org/10.3390/nu15163583

Hunter, D. C., Skinner, M. A., & A. Ross Ferguson. (2016). *Kiwifruit and health*. 239–269. https://doi.org/10.1016/b978-0-12-802972-5.00012-3

Hussain, M., Sabri, R., Muhammad Zia-Ul-Haq, & Riaz, M. (2023). Celery. *Springer EBooks*, 1165–1190. https://doi.org/10.1007/978-3-031-35403-8_45

Indresh K. , Priya Y. , Madhulika G., Hema P. (2022). Impact of Heat on Naturally Present Digestive Enzymes in Food. International Journal of Food, Nutrition and Dietetics Volume 10 Number 2, May – August 2022. https://www.researchgate.net/profile/Indresh-Kumar-5/publication/360412279_Impact_of_Heat_on_Naturally_Present_Digestive_Enzymes_in_Food/links/6274ec20973bbb29cc668221/Impact-of-Heat-on-Naturally-Present-Digestive-Enzymes-in-Food.pdf

Ivarsson, J., Pecorelli, A., Mary Ann Lila, & Valacchi, G. (2023). Blueberry Supplementation and Skin Health. *Antioxidants*, *12*(6), 1261–1261. https://doi.org/10.3390/antiox12061261

Javanbakht, P., Yazdi, F., R., Taghizadeh, F., Khadivi, F., Hamidabadi, H., G., Kashani, I., R., Zarini, D., & Mojaverrostami, S. (2023). Quercetin as a possible complementary therapy in multiple sclerosis: Anti-oxidative, anti-inflammatory and remyelination potential properties. *Heliyon*. https://www.cell.com/heliyon/pdf/S2405-8440(23)08949-1.pdf

Johnson, S. A., Figueroa, A., Navaei, N., Wong, A., Kalfon, R., Ormsbee, L. T., Feresin, R. G., Elam, M. L., Hooshmand, S., Payton, M. E., & Arjmandi, B. H. (2015). Daily Blueberry Consumption Improves Blood Pressure and Arterial Stiffness in Postmenopausal Women with Pre- and Stage 1-Hypertension: A Randomized, Double-Blind, Placebo-Controlled Clinical Trial. *Journal of the Academy of Nutrition and Dietetics*, *115*(3), 369–377. https://doi.org/10.1016/j.jand.2014.11.001

Jones, K. M., & de Brauw, A. (2015). Using Agriculture to Improve Child Health: Promoting Orange Sweet Potatoes Reduces Diarrhea. *World Development*, *74*, 15–24. https://doi.org/10.1016/j.worlddev.2015.04.007

Kang, J. H., Willett, W. C., Rosner, B. A., Buys, E., Wiggs, J. L., & Pasquale, L. R. (2016). Association of Dietary Nitrate Intake With Primary Open-Angle Glaucoma. *JAMA Ophthalmology*, *134*(3), 294. https://doi.org/10.1001/jamaophthalmol.2015.5601

Kelley, D., Adkins, Y., & Laugero, K. (2018). A Review of the Health Benefits of Cherries. *Nutrients*, *10*(3), 368. https://doi.org/10.3390/nu10030368

Khalid Mohammed Khan, Hameed, S., & Shamim, S. (2023). *Natural Products to Cure Bad Breath*. 217–252. https://doi.org/10.1002/9781394167197.ch12

Khan, N., Fahad, S., Naushad, M., & Faisal, S. (2020). Pomegranates Economics and Medicinal Aspects in the World. *SSRN Electronic Journal*. https://doi.org/10.2139/ssrn.3597891

Khan, K., M., Hameed, S., & Shamim, S. (2023). *Natural Products to Cure Bad Breath*. 217–252. https://doi.org/10.1002/9781394167197.ch12

Khatri, J., Mills, C. E., Maskell, P., Odongerel, C., & Webb, A. J. (2016). It is rocket science - why dietary nitrate is hard to "beet"!Part I: twists and turns in the realization of the nitrate-nitrite-NO pathway. *British Journal of Clinical Pharmacology*, *83*(1), 129–139. https://doi.org/10.1111/bcp.12913

Kim, D.-B., Shin, G.-H., Kim, J.-M., Kim, Y.-H., Lee, J.-H., Lee, J. S., Song, H.-J., Choe, S. Y., Park, I.-J., Cho, J.-H., & Lee, O.-H. (2016). Antioxidant and anti-ageing activities of citrus-based juice mixture. *Food Chemistry*, *194*, 920–927. https://doi.org/10.1016/j.foodchem.2015.08.094

Kim, J.-E., & Cho, K.-O. (2019). Functional Nutrients for Epilepsy. *Nutrients*, *11*(6). https://doi.org/10.3390/nu11061309

Kooti, W., & Daraei, N. (2017). A Review of the Antioxidant Activity of Celery (Apium graveolens L). *Journal of Evidence-Based Complementary & Alternative Medicine*, *22*(4), 1029–1034. https://doi.org/10.1177/2156587217717415

Kostiuchenko, O., Kravchenko, N., Markus, J., Burleigh, S., Fedkiv, O., Cao, L., Letasiova, S., Skibo, G., Fåk Hållenius, F., & Prykhodko, O. (2022). Effects of Proteases from Pineapple and Papaya on Protein Digestive Capacity and Gut Microbiota in Healthy C57BL/6 Mice and Dose-Manner Response on Mucosal Permeability in Human Reconstructed Intestinal 3D Tissue Model. *Metabolites*, *12*(11), 1027. https://doi.org/10.3390/metabo12111027

Koutsos, A., Riccadonna, S., Ulaszewska, M. M., Franceschi, P., Trošt, K., Galvin, A., Braune, T., Fava, F., Perenzoni, D., Mattivi, F., Tuohy, K. M., & Lovegrove, J. A. (2019). Two apples a day lower serum cholesterol and improve cardiometabolic biomarkers in mildly hypercholesterolemic adults: a randomized, controlled, crossover trial. *The American Journal of Clinical Nutrition*, *111*(2), 307–318. https://doi.org/10.1093/ajcn/nqz282

Kristo, A., Klimis-Zacas, D., & Sikalidis, A. (2016). Protective Role of Dietary Berries in Cancer. *Antioxidants*, *5*(4), 37. https://doi.org/10.3390/antiox5040037

Kukadia, S., Dehbi, H., Tillin, T., Coady, E., Chaturvedi, N., Hughes, A., D. (2019). A Double-Blind Placebo-Controlled Crossover Study of the Effect of Beetroot Juice Containing Dietary Nitrate

on Aortic and Brachial Blood Pressure Over 24 h. *Front. Physiol., 03 February 2019 Sec. Vascular Physiology Volume 10 - 2019.*
https://doi.org/10.3389/fphys.2019.00047

Kumar, A., Kumar, V., Gull, A., & Nayik, G. A. (2020). Tomato (Solanum Lycopersicon). *Antioxidants in Vegetables and Nuts - Properties and Health Benefits*, 191–207.
https://doi.org/10.1007/978-981-15-7470-2_10

Łuczaj, W., Moniuszko, A., Jarocka-karpowicz, I., Pancewicz, S., Andrisic, L., Zarkovic, N., & Skrzydlewska, E. (2015). Tick-borne encephalitis – lipid peroxidation and its consequences. *Scandinavian Journal of Clinical and Laboratory Investigation, 76*(1), 1–9.
https://doi.org/10.3109/00365513.2015.1084040

Luo, X., Zhang, H., Duan, Y., & Chen, G. (2018). Protective effects of radish (Raphanus sativus L.) leaves extract against hydrogen peroxide-induced oxidative damage in human fetal lung fibroblast (MRC-5) cells. *Biomedicine & Pharmacotherapy, 103*, 406–414.
https://doi.org/10.1016/j.biopha.2018.04.049

Ma, L., Sun, Z., Zeng, Y., Luo, M., & Yang, J. (2018). Molecular Mechanism and Health Role of Functional Ingredients in Blueberry for Chronic Disease in Human Beings. *International Journal of Molecular Sciences, 19*(9), 2785.
https://doi.org/10.3390/ijms19092785

Mahaveer, S., Prerak, B. (2019). A Review On Proactive Pomegranate One Of The Healthiest Foods. International Journal of Chemical Studies 2019; 7(3): 189-194.
https://d1wqtxts1xzle7.cloudfront.net/89512507/7-2-254-757-libre.pdf?1660287097=&response-content-disposition=inline%3B+filename%3DA_review_on_proactive_pomegranate_one_of.pdf&Expires=1714037595&Signature=QfCrfbUB~Vbn11pbfxNG~v~2YfxMRkEGC7ZtNELIl1HgxSWP0aHwAEAds07KKm2MRZiTzy-~B4Os2fF6zNp5mS4r1FIP3pvK-3I31~OLWSSuzRD6cdqGoicaxZFCu7usvI9s2cOliJqtGqdO9RYsKwXWhJVQlcvbkpYvBFr5laT9JqW1OR5Qj2KmNsSGRUvJFvV7gpBuFzJkWHqT~Bi95nH1MUBzzPr9NEK5ekUCjRkyPrxss4XabsQBg-PZlaUl6BUf5LxLT7OP8ZgN43d53zLB2gvGxonItI2V2N9ird3IHWoEjWjra2DXEqLhDxj2~HulZtGl27ZaiB2j1528eg__&Key-Pair-Id=APKAJLOHF5GGSLRBV4ZA

Mahboubi, M. (2020). Sambucus nigra (black elder) as alternative treatment for cold and flu. *Advances in Traditional Medicine, 21.*
https://doi.org/10.1007/s13596-020-00469-z

Manna, P., & Kalita, J. (2016). Beneficial role of vitamin K supplementation on insulin sensitivity, glucose metabolism, and the reduced risk of type 2 diabetes: A review. *Nutrition, 32*(7-8), 732–739.
https://doi.org/10.1016/j.nut.2016.01.011

Mamgain, P., Kandwal, A., & Mamgain, R. K. (2016). Comparative Evaluation of Triphala and Ela Decoction With 0.2% Chlorhexidine as Mouthwash in the Treatment of Plaque-Induced

Gingivitis and Halitosis: A Randomized Controlled Clinical Trial. *Journal of Evidence-Based Complementary & Alternative Medicine, 22*(3), 468–472.
https://doi.org/10.1177/2156587216679532

Manfredini, R., De Giorgi, A., Storari, A., & Fabbian, F. (2016). Pears and renal stones: possible weapon for prevention? A comprehensive narrative review. *European Review for Medical and Pharmacological Sciences, 20*(3), 414–425.
https://pubmed.ncbi.nlm.nih.gov/26914114/

Maoto, M. M., Beswa, D., & Jideani, A. I. O. (2019). Watermelon as a potential fruit snack. *International Journal of Food Properties, 22*(1), 355–370.
https://doi.org/10.1080/10942912.2019.1584212

Masud Parvez, G. M., & Akanda, K. M. (2019, January 1). *Chapter 1 - Foods and Arthritis: An Overview* (R. R. Watson & V. R. Preedy, Eds.). ScienceDirect; Academic Press.
https://www.sciencedirect.com/science/article/abs/pii/B9780128138205000015

Miyazaki, N., Katsura, R., Hamada, K., & Suzutani, T. (2020). Blueberry Prevents the Bladder Dysfunction in Bladder Outlet Obstruction Rats by Attenuating Oxidative Stress and Suppressing Bladder Remodeling. *Nutrients, 12*(5), 1285.
https://doi.org/10.3390/nu12051285

Medeiros, I., de Oliveira, G. L. R., de Queiroz, J. L. C., de Carvalho Gomes, C., de Carvalho, F. M. C., de Souza Lima, M. C. J., Serquiz, A. C., de Andrade Santos, P. P., da Silva Camillo, C., Maciel, B. L. L., de Araújo Morais, A. H., & Passos, T. S. (2020). Safety and bioactive potential of nanoparticles containing Cantaloupe melon (Cucumis melo L.) carotenoids in an experimental model of chronic inflammation. *Biotechnology Reports, 28*, e00567.
https://doi.org/10.1016/j.btre.2020.e00567

Miles, E. A., & Calder, P. C. (2021). Effects of Citrus Fruit Juices and Their Bioactive Components on Inflammation and Immunity: A Narrative Review. *Frontiers in Immunology, 12*.
https://doi.org/10.3389/fimmu.2021.712608

Mirzababaei, A., Khorsha, F., Togha, M., Yekaninejad, M. S., Okhovat, A. A., & Mirzaei, K. (2018). Associations between adherence to dietary approaches to stop hypertension (DASH) diet and migraine headache severity and duration among women. *Nutritional Neuroscience, 23*(5), 335–342.
https://doi.org/10.1080/1028415x.2018.1503848

Mlcek, J., Jurikova, T., Skrovankova, S., & Sochor, J. (2016). Quercetin and Its Anti-Allergic Immune Response. *Molecules, 21*(5), 623.
https://doi.org/10.3390/molecules21050623

Mohamed Ali, M. F., Swar, M. O., & Osman, A. M. (2016). Treatment of iron deficiency anaemia with the natural hematinic Carbaodeim. *Sudanese Journal of Paediatrics, 16*(1), 37–44.
https://www.ncbi.nlm.nih.gov/pmc/articles/PMC5025931/

Mulwa, P. M., Njue, W., & Ng'ang'a, M. (2020). Assessment of L-Citrulline, L-Arginine and L-Glutamic Acid Content in Selected Fruits, Vegetables, Seeds, and Nuts Sold in Markets in Nairobi City County, Kenya. *European Journal of Agriculture and Food Sciences, 2*(5). https://doi.org/10.24018/ejfood.2020.2.5.100

Mrowicka, M., Mrowicki, J., Kucharska, E., & Majsterek, I. (2022). Lutein and Zeaxanthin and Their Roles in Age-Related Macular Degeneration—Neurodegenerative Disease. *Nutrients, 14*(4), 827. https://doi.org/10.3390/nu14040827

Nadeem, M., Maham Navida, Ameer, K., Iqbal, A., Malik, F., Nadeem, M., Fatima, H., Ahmed, A., & Din, A. (2022). *A comprehensive review on the watermelon phytochemical profile and their bioactive and therapeutic effects. 29*(4), 546–576. https://doi.org/10.11002/kjfp.2022.29.4.546

Nakagawa, T., Lanaspa, M. A., & Johnson, R. J. (2019). The effects of fruit consumption in patients with hyperuricaemia or gout. *Rheumatology, 58*(7), 1133–1141. https://doi.org/10.1093/rheumatology/kez128

Naureen, Z., Dhuli, K., Donato, K., Aquilanti, B., Velluti, V., Matera, G., Iaconelli, A., & Bertelli, M. (2022). Foods of the Mediterranean diet: citrus, cucumber and grape. *Journal of preventive medicine and hygiene, 63*(2 Suppl 3), E21–E27. https://doi.org/10.15167/2421-4248/jpmh2022.63.2S3.2743

Nesello, L. A. N., Beleza, M. L. M. L., Mariot, M., Mariano, L. N. B., de Souza, P., Campos, A., Cechinel-Filho, V., Andrade, S. F., & da Silva, L. M. (2017). Gastroprotective Value of Berries: Evidences from Methanolic Extracts of Morus nigra and Rubus niveus Fruits. *Gastroenterology Research and Practice, 2017,* 1–8. https://doi.org/10.1155/2017/7089697

Newerli-Guz, J., Śmiechowska, M., Drzewiecka, A., & Tylingo, R. (2023). Bioactive Ingredients with Health-Promoting Properties of Strawberry Fruit (Fragaria x ananassa Duchesne). *Molecules (Basel, Switzerland), 28*(6), 2711. https://doi.org/10.3390/molecules28062711

Oki, T., Kano, M., Ishikawa, F., Goto, K., Watanabe, O., & Suda, I. (2017). Double-blind, placebo-controlled pilot trial of anthocyanin-rich purple sweet potato beverage on serum hepatic biomarker levels in healthy Caucasians with borderline hepatitis. *European Journal of Clinical Nutrition, 71*(2), 290–292. https://doi.org/10.1038/ejcn.2016.153

Pamphlett R, Doble PA, Bishop DP (2021). Mercury in the human thyroid gland: Potential implications for thyroid cancer, autoimmune thyroiditis, and hypothyroidism. PLoS ONE 16(2): e0246748. https://doi.org/10.1371/journal.pone.0246748

Prasad, K., Haq, R., Bansal, V., Siddiqui, M., W., Ilahy, R. (2016). Carrot: Secondary Metabolites and Their Prospective Health Benefits. Plant Secondary Metabolites (pp.88). Apple Academic Press.
https://www.taylorfrancis.com/chapters/edit/10.1201/9781315366319-13/carrot-secondary-metabolites-prospective-health-benefits-kamlesh-prasad-raees-ul-haq-vasudha-bansal-mohammed-wasim-siddiqui-riadh-ilahy

Pomilio, A. B., Szewczuk, N. A., & Duchowicz, P. R. (2022). Dietary anthocyanins balance immune signs in osteoarthritis and obesity – update of human *in vitro* studies and clinical trials. *Critical Reviews in Food Science and Nutrition*, 1–39.
https://doi.org/10.1080/10408398.2022.2124948

Reiszadeh-Jahromi, S., Haddadi, M., Mousavi, P., & Sanadgol, S., (2022). Prophylactic effects of cucurbitacin B in the EAE Model of multiple sclerosis by adjustment of STAT3/IL-23/IL-17 axis and improvement of neuropsychological symptoms. *Metabolic Brain Disease*, *37*(8), 2937–2953.
https://doi.org/10.1007/s11011-022-01083-5

Ribeiro, J. A., dos Santos Pereira, E., de Oliveira Raphaelli, C., Radünz, M., Camargo, T. M., da Rocha Concenço, F. I. G., Cantillano, R. F. F., Fiorentini, Â. M., & Nora, L. (2021). Application of prebiotics in apple products and potential health benefits. *Journal of Food Science and Technology*.
https://doi.org/10.1007/s13197-021-05062-z

Rodrigues, L., Palma, L., Tavares Marques, L., & Bujan Varela, J. (2015). Dietary water affects human skin hydration and biomechanics. *Clinical, Cosmetic and Investigational Dermatology*, *8*, 413.
https://doi.org/10.2147/ccid.s86822

Rolnik, A., & Olas, B. (2020). Vegetables from Cucurbitaceae family and their products; positive effect on human health. *Nutrition*, 110788.
https://doi.org/10.1016/j.nut.2020.110788

Ritz, T., Werchan, C. A., Kroll, J. L., & Rosenfield, D. (2019). Beetroot juice supplementation for the prevention of cold symptoms associated with stress: A proof-of-concept study. *Physiology & Behavior*, *202*, 45–51.
https://doi.org/10.1016/j.physbeh.2019.01.015

Saban, G. (n.d.). *The Benefits of Brassica Vegetables on Human Health*.
https://www.article.scholarena.co/The-Benefits-of-Brassica-Vegetables-on-Human-Health.pdf

Sadikan M., Z., Mohamad M., N., Asri2, Haryati Ahmad Hairi H., A., & Singar A., S (2023). Relevance and Use of Honey and Lemon Water for Cough . Compilation Of Research Papers On Stem - October 2023 (Science, Technology, Enginerring & Mathematics).
https://www.researchgate.net/profile/Muhammad-Zulfiqah-Sadikan/publication/375117673_Relevance_and_Use_of_Honey_and_Lemon_Water_for_Cough/links/6541a9dc0426ef6369edf27b/Relevance-and-Use-of-Honey-and-Lemon-Water-for-Cough.pdf

Sadeghi, M., Kabiri, S., Amerizadeh, A., Heshmat-Ghahdarijani, K., Masoumi, G., Teimouri-Jervekani, Z., & Amirpour, A. (2022). Anethum graveolens L. (Dill) Effect on Human Lipid Profile: An Updated Systematic Review. *Current Problems in Cardiology, 47*(11), 101072. https://doi.org/10.1016/j.cpcardiol.2021.101072

Santoyo-Sánchez, A., Aponte-Castillo, J. A., Parra-Peña, R. I., & Ramos-Peñafiel, C. O. (2015). Dietary recommendations in patients with deficiency anaemia. *Revista Médica Del Hospital General de México, 78*(3), 144–150. https://doi.org/10.1016/j.hgmx.2015.06.002

Schell, J., Scofield, R. H., Barrett, J. R., Kurien, B. T., Betts, N., Lyons, T. J., Zhao, Y. D., & Basu, A. (2017). Strawberries Improve Pain and Inflammation in Obese Adults with Radiographic Evidence of Knee Osteoarthritis. *Nutrients, 9*(9), 949. https://doi.org/10.3390/nu9090949

Sahu, T., & Sahu, J. (2015). Cucumis sativus (cucumber): a review on its pharmacological activity. *Journal of Applied Pharmaceutical Research, 3*(1), 04–09. https://www.japtronline.com/index.php/joapr/article/view/46

Salehi, B., Venditti, A., Frezza, C., Yücetepe, A., Altuntaş, Ü., Uluata, S., Butnariu, M., Sarac, I., Shaheen, S., A. Petropoulos, S., R. Matthews, K., Sibel Kılıç, C., Atanassova, M., Oluwaseun Adetunji, C., Oluwaseun Ademiluyi, A., Özçelik, B., Valere Tsouh Fokou, P., Martins, N., C. Cho, W., & Sharifi-Rad, J. (2019). Apium Plants: Beyond Simple Food and Phytopharmacological Applications. *Applied Sciences, 9(17)*, 3547. https://doi.org/10.3390/app9173547

Salvo E., D., Gangemi, S., Genovese, C., Cicero, N., & Casciaro, M. (2023). Polyphenols from Mediterranean Plants: Biological Activities for Skin Photoprotection in Atopic Dermatitis, Psoriasis, and Chronic Urticaria. *Plants, 12*(20), 3579–3579. https://doi.org/10.3390/plants12203579

Sarshar, S., Sendker, J., Qin, X., Goycoolea, F. M., Asadi Karam, M. R., Habibi, M., Bouzari, S., Dobrindt, U., & Hensel, A. (2018). Antiadhesive hydroalcoholic extract from Apium graveolens fruits prevents bladder and kidney infection against uropathogenic E. coli. *Fitoterapia, 127*, 237–244. https://doi.org/10.1016/j.fitote.2018.02.029

Sarwar, S., Ayyub, M, A., Rezgui, M., Nisar, S., & Jilani, M., I., (2016). Parsley: A review of habitat, phytochemistry, ethnopharmacology and biological activities. *International Journal of Chemical and Biochemical Sciences (ISSN 2226-9614).* https://d1wqtxts1xzle7.cloudfront.net/87763441/6-IJCBS-16-09-06-libre.pdf?1655708576=&response-content-disposition=inline%3B+filename%3DParsley_A_review_of_habitat_phytochemist.pdf&Expires=1714459331&Signature=JbLB9jyOM2OPXVt5FYRrv8HW7qAv1MfpeNa9qUjTSAeBHn7SFuDw-LSnAXw16mUoo4R6ACXMhtzi51BHx34ovj6R3hJzEebfgvO0X6bSqqaYL2pZYP1hNGAviJ6i4KORw25tyYf7fTI6375E3S2DW8PgCE2EtUA4iBnuhpmb3LU3n2YS9XjKC-K9azNlznvaPFWEld8QMWjPgORO1dqgklqOMDzjcd~KWP4dTEHp3Af8A39NPzw1v~YBS-jogOvIh946gewoZdDvYviwpXxz3YhuOt49UEkkPa1zsYiZcCO4WHF151BtQmitV-20eobvBW7CTtVz4v1r-GuT0rooVQ__&Key-Pair-Id=APKAJLOHF5GGSLRBV4ZA

Scandar, S., Zadra, C., & Marcotullio, M. C. (2023). Coriander (Coriandrum sativum) Polyphenols and Their Nutraceutical Value against Obesity and Metabolic Syndrome. *Molecules*, *28*(10), 4187.
https://doi.org/10.3390/molecules28104187

Schulz, R. M., Ahuja, N. K., & Slavin, J. L. (2022). Effectiveness of Nutritional Ingredients on Upper Gastrointestinal Conditions and Symptoms: A Narrative Review. *Nutrients*, *14*(3), 672.
https://doi.org/10.3390/nu14030672

Shankar, S., Gopinath, P., Roja, E., (2022). Role of Spices and Herbs in Controlling Dental Problems. *Research Journal of Pharmacology and Pharmacodynamics 14(1):23-8.*
doi: 10.52711/2321-5836.2022.00004

Shafi, S., Murtaza, I., Mukherjee, G., & Singh, D. (2022). A Review on Kale as a Substantial Meal. *NeuroQuantology, Volume 20, Issue 8: 2168-2172.*
https://www.researchgate.net/profile/Divya-Singh-38/publication/372960073_A_Review_on_Kale_as_a_Substantial_Meal/links/64d1b654806a9e4e5cf75d19/A-Review-on-Kale-as-a-Substantial-Meal.pdf

Shoaib, M., Mounika, J., Wahid, M., Vandana, S., Chakrapani, B., Sowmya, S., & Pradesh, A. (2016). EVALUATION OF ANTI ULCER ACTIVITY OF ACETONE EXTRACT OF Brassica oleracea IN ALBINO RATS. *International Journal of Trends in Pharmacy and Life Sciences*, *2*(3), 923–932.
https://web.archive.org/web/20180422091419id_/http://ijtpls.com/wp-content/uploads/2016/04/IJTPLS-2015-Vol-23-Shoib-923-9322.pdf

Siener, R. (2021). Nutrition and Kidney Stone Disease. *Nutrients*, *13*(6), 1917.
https://doi.org/10.3390/nu13061917

Silva, H. (2020). A Descriptive Overview of the Medical Uses Given to Mentha Aromatic Herbs throughout History. *Biology*, *9*(12), 484.
https://doi.org/10.3390/biology9120484

Smith, K. S., Raney, S. V., Greene, M. W., & Frugé, A. D. (2019). Development and Validation of the Dietary Habits and Colon Cancer Beliefs Survey (DHCCBS): An Instrument Assessing Health Beliefs Related to Red Meat and Green Leafy Vegetable Consumption. *Journal of Oncology*, *2019*, 1–7.
https://doi.org/10.1155/2019/2326808

Stevens, S. L. (2021). Fat-Soluble Vitamins. *The Nursing Clinics of North America*, *56*(1), 33–45.
https://doi.org/10.1016/j.cnur.2020.10.003

Stowe, C. B. (2011). The effects of pomegranate juice consumption on blood pressure and cardiovascular health. *Complementary Therapies in Clinical Practice*, *17*(2), 113–115.
https://doi.org/10.1016/j.ctcp.2010.09.004

Sujana, K., Tejaswini, K., Lakshmi, S., Tejaswini, S., & Sri, S. (2016). Cranberry fruit: An update review. ~ 5 ~ *International Journal of Herbal Medicine*, *4*(3), 5-08.
https://www.florajournal.com/archives/2016/vol4issue3/PartA/4-3-2.pdf

Suleria, H.A.R., Goyal, M.R., & Ul Ain, H.B.(2022). Bioactive Compounds from Multifarious Natural Foods for Human Health. In *Apple Academic Press eBooks*. https://doi.org/10.1201/9781003189763

Szpadel, K., Jabłońska, I., Pizon, M., & Woźniak, M. (2022). Promising Strategies in Plant-Derived Treatments of Psoriasis-Update of In Vitro, In Vivo, and Clinical Trials Studies. *Molecules*, *27*(3), 591. https://doi.org/10.3390/molecules27030591

Tabrizi, A., Dargahi, R., Tehrani Ghadim, S., Javadi, M., Rasouli Pirouzian, H., Azizi, A., & Homayouni Rad, A. (2020). Functional laxative foods: Concepts, trends and health benefits. *Studies in Natural Products Chemistry*, *66*, 305-330. https://doi.org/10.1016/B978-0-12-817907-9.00011-8

Taneja, M., & Qureshi, S. (2015). Holistic approach to deafness. *Indian Journal of Otology*, *21*(1), 1. https://doi.org/10.4103/0971-7749.152847

Tardy, A.-L., Pouteau, E., Marquez, D., Yilmaz, C., & Scholey, A. (2020). Vitamins and minerals for energy, fatigue and cognition: A narrative review of the biochemical and clinical evidence. *Nutrients*, *12*(1), 228. https://doi.org/10.3390/nu12010228

Temitope, J. (2019). Vitamins as Antioxidants. *Journal of Food Science and Nutrition Research*, *2*(3), 214–235. https://www.fortuneonline.org/articles/vitamins-as-antioxidants.html?url=vitamins-as-antioxidants

Trautwein, E. A., Koppenol, W. P., de Jong, A., Hiemstra, H., Vermeer, M. A., Noakes, M., & Luscombe-Marsh, N. D. (2018). Plant sterols lower LDL-cholesterol and triglycerides in dyslipidemic individuals with or at risk of developing type 2 diabetes; a randomized, double-blind, placebo-controlled study. *Nutrition & Diabetes*, *8*. https://doi.org/10.1038/s41387-018-0039-8

Varilla, C., Marcone, M., Paiva, L., & Baptista, J. (2021). Bromelain, a Group of Pineapple Proteolytic Complex Enzymes (Ananas comosus) and Their Possible Therapeutic and Clinical Effects. A Summary. *Foods*, *10*(10), 2249. https://doi.org/10.3390/foods10102249

Vervloet, M. G., Sezer, S., Massy, Z. A., Johansson, L., Cozzolino, M., & Fouque, D. (2016). The role of phosphate in kidney disease. *Nature Reviews Nephrology*, *13*(1), 27–38. https://doi.org/10.1038/nrneph.2016.164

Vora, R., Khushboo, M., Shah, A., Patel, D., & Patel, T. (2020). Diet in dermatology: a review. *Egyptian Journal of Dermatology and Venerology*, *40*(2), 69. https://doi.org/10.4103/ejdv.ejdv_48_19

Wallace, T. C., Bailey, R. L., Blumberg, J. B., Burton-Freeman, B., Chen, C-y. O., Crowe-White, K. M., Drewnowski, A., Hooshmand, S., Johnson, E., Lewis, R., Murray, R., Shapses, S. A., & Wang, D. D. (2019). Fruits, vegetables, and health: A comprehensive narrative, umbrella review of the

science and recommendations for enhanced public policy to improve intake. *Critical Reviews in Food Science and Nutrition, 60*(13), 1–38.
https://doi.org/10.1080/10408398.2019.1632258

Wardani, R. S., Schellack, N., Govender, T., Dhulap, A. N., Utami, P., Malve, V., & Wong, Y. C. (2023). Treatment of the common cold with herbs used in Ayurveda and Jamu: monograph review and the science of ginger, liquorice, turmeric and peppermint. *Drugs in context, 12*, 2023-2-12.
https://doi.org/10.7573/dic.2023-2-12

Wigner, P., Bijak, M., & Saluk-Bijak, J. (2022). Clinical Potential of Fruit in Bladder Cancer Prevention and Treatment. *Nutrients, 14*(6), 1132.
https://doi.org/10.3390/nu14061132

Wise, R. A., Holbrook, J. T., Criner, G., Sethi, S., Sobharani Rayapudi, Sudini, K. R., Sugar, E. A., Burke, A., Rajesh Thimmulappa, Singh, A., Talalay, P., Fahey, J. W., Berenson, C. S., Jacobs, M. R., & Shyam Biswal. (2016). Lack of Effect of Oral Sulforaphane Administration on Nrf2 Expression in COPD: A Randomized, Double-Blind, Placebo Controlled Trial. *PloS One, 11*(11), e0163716–e0163716.
https://doi.org/10.1371/journal.pone.0163716

Yadav Akshay R., Mohite Shrinivas K., Magdum Chandrakant S. (2020) Preparation and evaluation of antibacterial herbal mouthwash against oral pathogens. *Asian Journal of Research in Pharmaceutical Science, 10*(3).
https://www.indianjournals.com/ijor.aspx?target=ijor:ajrps&volume=10&issue=3&article=005

Zhu, J., & Du, C. (2019). Could grape-based food supplements prevent the development of chronic kidney disease? *Critical Reviews in Food Science and Nutrition*, 1–9.
https://doi.org/10.1080/10408398.2019.1676195

Zhexenbay, N., A., Nabiyeva, Z., Kizatova, M., & Iskakova, G. (2020). USING PECTIN AS HEAVY METALS DETOXIFICATION AGENT TO REDUCE ENVIRONMENTAL CONTAMINATION AND HEALTH RISKS. *Procedia Environmental Science, Engineering and Management, 7*(4), 551–562.
https://www.procedia-esem.eu/pdf/issues/2020/no4/8_60_Zhexenay_20.pdf

Zuraini, N. Z. A., Sekar, M., Wu, Y. S., Gan, S. H., Bonam, S. R., Mat Rani, N. N. I., Begum, M. Y., Lum, P. T., Subramaniyan, V., Fuloria, N. K., & Fuloria, S. (2021). Promising Nutritional Fruits Against Cardiovascular Diseases: An Overview of Experimental Evidence and Understanding Their Mechanisms of Action. *Vascular Health and Risk Management, Volume 17*, 739–769.
https://doi.org/10.2147/vhrm.s328096

Made in the USA
Monee, IL
10 October 2024

67562883R00070